The commissary is our prison store. It sells food-stuffs, like tea, rice, canned vegetables, sodas, cookies, and candy bars, as well as soaps and shampoos, paper and pencils, cigarettes, and stamps. Inmates may go to this store once every two weeks.

An officer stands at the grating with the inmates and gives orders to everyone and anyone who enters the area.

"Don't stand there. Move over. No. A little to the left. Not like that. More to the right. Where's your I.D.? Let me see it. Don't hand it to me. Put it away. Don't leave it there. Now, who's next? Line up. Not there! Pass the sheet in under the grate on the left side."

"But we've always put it on the right side."

"Not since yesterday. Now we put it on the left and pick up on the right."

"This place is insane."

"Who did you say was insane?"

"Nobody."

"Well, watch it. Whose basket is that? You can't leave it there."

"It's where you told me last time."

"Move it. Not there. Up there. Not so near. Over on the side. Who's next. Hurry up."

"Oh, oh. I forget to mark Kleenex. I need a box of Kleenex, too."

"You know the rules. After the list passes under the grating, there are no changes. No additions. No subtractions."

"Up yours, you old bitch." CHECKOUT

JEAN HARRIS

THEY ALWAYS CALL US
LADIES

Stories From Prison

ZEBRA BOOKS
KENSINGTON PUBLISHING CORP.

Some names have been changed to protect what little privacy prisoners have. — JH

ZEBRA BOOKS

are published by

Kensington Publishing Corp.
475 Park Avenue South
New York, NY 10016

First Zebra Books printing: May, 1990

Printed in the United States of America

To those women of Bedford who should not be in prison, and to those staff members at Bedford with the intelligence and integrity to treat all humans with dignity. God willing, there will someday be fewer of the former and more of the latter.

Acknowledgments

I am deeply grateful to those who helped me to gather background information for this book: Reverend Dale Baker, Sue Cullman, Joan Devareux, Ronnie Eldridge, Donna Gilton, Father James Gorman, Alice Lacey, Gay and Charles Lord, Kathleen O'Leary, and Rose Palladino.

Organizations that have most generously shared information with me include The Correctional Association of New York, The Elizabeth Fry Association of Canada, The Guttmacher Institute, the United States Department of Justice, the Urban League, and the Westchester Historical Society.

My special thanks go to Estelle B. Freedman whose excellent book, *Their Sisters' Keepers*, especially its footnotes, made me feel I had taken at least a peek into the archives; to Barbara Carlton who has typed this text at least twice, always with a smile, and always under difficult conditions, when we were lucky enough to have a ribbon for the typewriter; and to Robert Stewart, who has now gone through the very tiresome process, twice, of going to prison to edit a book. His kindness, his patience, his wisdom, the way he told me something wasn't good enough without hurting my frayed feelings — all make him a very special friend and editor.

Contents

Civilization is no accident; it requires the constant creation of new kinds of social enrichment. It's what people actually do that constitutes culture, not the acceptance and classification of a canon by a relatively small body of theorists; it is the making of an art, not its collection and preservation.

Melville

Introduction

Maybe it started with Bettye, Bettye with two e's, last name unknown. She had scratched and poked her name into the putty around a pane of glass in her cell window. It has to have been at least twenty years ago. It could have been fifty years ago. No one had lived in the building for years when I moved into Bettye's cell on New Year's Day, 1983.

To the authorities I am known as #81-G-98, which means I was the ninety-eighth prisoner to arrive at Bedford Hills Correctional Facility in 1981. Today I live on cell block 112A. If this were twenty years ago I would be called "the girl in cell 10 A." But now I'm "the lady in cell 10 A." Maybe we have the feminists to thank for that breakthrough.

Though one may imagine prisoners with nothing but time on their hands, I usually have a full day. Like you, before I go to work, I clean house. My room is a cell, but I prefer to think of it as a room. It is ten feet deep and six and a half feet wide. I now know it is a palace compared to cells of not too many years ago, and possibly cells of the future as well. Unlike cells in most men's prisons, it has four walls, no open bars to preclude all pretense of privacy. Its metal door is opened and closed by a guard from a station at the

13

head of the corridor. For some reason that station is called "the bubble," though it isn't a bubble in any sense of the word—just a big desk on a raised platform.

My bed fits across the room under the window. It probably hasn't been moved for years since it lacks a footboard and is propped up at the end by an old wooden box. My bed board, recommended by the doctor, I keep pushed out six inches along the wall, thus making a six-foot-long bookshelf. It also makes the mattress more lopsided than it already is, but the shelf makes up in convenience for the discomfort.

Each cell contains, in addition to the bed, a small sink and toilet, a chair, a metal lockbox and a metal nightstand with a tiny drawer and a shelf. It is interesting that a place which professes to encourage people to learn, and in fact often does, where teaching is provided for everything from learning the alphabet to earning a bachelor's degree, provides neither desk nor bookshelf for anyone. As a result, shelves are made out of boxes and anything else one is lucky enough to find, and creative enough to use. Unfortunately, creativity, no matter how innocent it may be, is not looked upon kindly in prison. My shelves are made of boards from board games that have been thrown away in the Children's Center after all the other parts are missing. I retrieve them from the trash as the treasures they are, and build my shelves, but I never know from day to day when they will be taken from me.

My day begins with the usual ritual of making my bed after we are awakened at 6:00 A.M. Making the bed is a little like making one of the bunk beds at our old family cottage in Canada. It involves climbing on the bed (since I can't walk around it) and trying to smooth a spread, made from a sheet, smoothly over a mattress that measures anywhere from one inch to seven inches thick, depending upon where the stuffing has gathered into large lumps. My pillow I open from time to time, pull the stuffing apart, fluff it, and put it back into the pillow, thus providing my head with a soft place to lie until the inside mats up again and the process must be repeated.

I take up my two tiny rugs, one a bath mat, the other a bequest to me from a friend leaving on parole. I wipe the floor carefully each day with a damp cloth, on my hands and knees. Unlike the chambermaids at the Copley Plaza I find this reassuring, an antique gesture that daily renews my membership in the female human race. I gather up any scraps from my work of the night before, put them in the little basket Sally sent me for flowers, walk to the recreation room and throw away the trash. I want the cell to be as inviting as a cell can be when I return in the afternoon sometime between 4:00 and 4:30. I spend the usual minute or two every morning trying to find my ID card, grab my green jacket and join the 7:45 line to the school building where I work most of each day.

The Children's Center, where I also work, is at the far end of the visiting room. Office work for the Center used to be done at one end of it, but we have outgrown what little space there was and now the office for the Children's Center is in the school building.

Once at work my job varies according to the time of year. From April to August, the children's Summer Program fills our time. From October to January, the children's Christmas and Hanukkah Program is our main effort. In between, we sew for the nursery, try to teach and encourage the young mothers to sew for themselves and their babies, teach parenting classes, acknowledge many inquiries that come to us about the Center, and I for one also putter. I try to keep files about the history of the Center, our Foster Care Program, the nursery, and other projects. I put things in notebooks and in a small white file cabinet so that they will be easy to find, and I keep a clipping file of any current subject about children, from how infants learn

15

to school dropouts, bonding of mother and child, teen-age pregnancy and others. They are sometimes used by our college students, and even by an occasional C.O. (corrections officer) for term papers and such. It pleases me when they are.

Meals are simple affairs for me. I eat in my cell to avoid the prison dining room which has all the ambiance and charm of the Chicago stockyards. We are allowed to have thirty-five pounds of food brought to us by family and friends in two deliveries per month. I can buy soup and macaroni and cheese and raisin bran at the prison commissary every other week, and every other week I can also purchase fresh fruits and vegetables at a small market in Bedford Hills that the prison has dealt with for many years. I drink powdered skimmed milk.

Sometimes I try to imagine what prison menu could lure me into the dining room again. There isn't one. Nectar and ambrosia couldn't persuade me to respond to the C.O.'s call, "On the chow, ladies. Last call. Keep moving. Keep moving. Show your ID. Where's your ID? No ID you don't go to the dining room. All right, keep moving, keep moving."

There's a small kitchenette in each housing unit where a good deal of cooking is done daily, especially by the Puerto Rican women. I don't cook because I don't like to, never did, and I especially don't like doing it surrounded by cockroaches on every side. The quiet civility and privacy of my own cell far outweighs the pleasure of food. I think it is fair to say I am the raisin bran queen of the East Coast.

From late afternoon until bedtime, I am free to choose my own activity. It's the dangerous time of the day because sunset always makes me a little sad, and time on one's hands can easily slide into time to think about oneself. In prison this is a dangerous thing to do. If you are wise you try to avoid it. As you can see, I don't always succeed, but then this is safe talk, just the setting of the scene.

Two afternoons a week I go to meetings of the ILC, Inmate Liaison Committee. One afternoon a month I go with five other elected inmate representatives to meet with the Superintendent and other administrative staff to review an agenda of inmate complaints and suggestions. Such meetings are required by State law.

Friday evenings three of us play bingo with the women on the mental ward, and thanks to a generous visiting schedule at Bedford I have a good many visitors. But there's still some daylight and six evenings left over. So I write. I write sitting on my bed, the first step being to find a safe place in one of the valleys of the mattress so I don't keep sliding down or falling off one of the humps. I write with a pen, usually a red-ink one since I have found over the years those are the ones least apt to be borrowed and not returned. Many of the women here tell me red signifies death. It is the color of blood, and they want no part of red ink. Occasionally, when someone asks to borrow a pen and I thoughtlessly hand her a red one, she may actually recoil from it in genuine fear.

The paper I use is whatever piece I can reach without having to get up and go through finding a valley again. Occasionally I remember the paper before I sit down, in which case I use a yellow legal pad and feel quite professional. I am also inclined to wake up in a glow of inspiration at all hours of the night and write down a splendid sentence. Then I spend the next four months figuring out where to put it. When I figure that out, I have trouble finding the envelope I wrote it on.

I reread everything I write out loud, because that's the only way I know if it says what I meant it to say. This has led many of the women around me to question my sanity. I also keep at least one ear cocked to pick up the conversations in the corridor which are always more colorful than anything I could contrive. And I write them down as fast as I can because a close approximation won't do.

To hear the conversations of the other numbered women on the corridor is to hear the story of their lives — the colorful, devious, funny, brave, obscene, tragic stories of their lives. It isn't eavesdropping. In fact, I have tried three times to get earplugs through the prison package room, but they're not allowed. What illegal mischief you can perpetrate with an earplug I don't know.

I've grown accustomed to the sounds of the corridor now, and, except when it descends into unspeakable obscenities or the loud, repetitive, threatening incantations of a psychopath, it's a little like having a story read to you all day long.

George Bernard Shaw said of Americans and Englishmen, "We are people separated by a common language." Black and white Americans are separated in much the same way. Black English is, if not a separate language, something close to it. If black people controlled the large majority of the wealth in America, and did most of the hiring and firing, their language would probably be the established language here. They don't, and it isn't. Yet white English is laced with many Black English words and colloquialisms. "Language," as Robert MacNeil observes, "reinforces feelings of social superiority or inferiority; it creates insiders and outsiders; it is a prop to vanity or a source of anxiety."

A corridor conversation that comes quickly to mind was one between Easy and Jo Jo. They were discussing their various illegal activities. Jo Jo began the conversation, as earnest as only she could sound. "Ah stole the meat, but ah always paid for ma vegetables," and ended with, "One thing ah never done. Ah never stole from ma mother. Tha's one thing you never do." Easy agreed. I remember that especially because three dear

18

old friends of mine upon hearing it said, "Gee, my mother was the one person I did steal from." I guess that comes under the heading of different cultural habits of black and white, or middle class and lower class. Or maybe we're all lying.

There's an aura of science fiction about prison. It's real, but it shouldn't be. It's easy to lose a sense of time in here — calendar time. Which day of the week it is doesn't matter too much. How many more years are left for you to live here is unthinkable. The seasons come and go with little to anticipate and much to dread, though the trees on the hillside were beautiful this year. Time takes on another dimension, somewhere in space. You know it's there, but you can't find it, and anyway you don't look very hard. The sameness of each day only you can change.

One of the many things for which I am grateful is that prison has not extinguished my sense of curiosity. The pleasure of searching, learning, fitting pieces together saves me from many of the horrors that the tedium of prison could reduce me to. Curiosity and caring have given birth to what follows.

Bettye's cell, Bettye with two e's, was in The Fiske Building, named in honor of the woman who had been head of the Board of Visitors for the New York Reformatory for Women when the building was built fifty-seven years ago. It was built to serve as the Segregation Housing Unit (SHU), where the naughtiest, most troubled and troublesome inmates were sent for punishment. That's what it was when Bettye was there. Now that the reformatory is gone, and on the same property stands a top security prison for women, Fiske is put to quite the opposite use. It is an honor cottage with special privileges for its twenty-six occupants. That's what it was when I arrived in Bettye's cell.

Today, the prison's SHU has none of the amenities

19

that were built into Fiske. It looks, as one might expect, quite ugly, a small, unimaginative cinder-block box with twelve cells for solitary confinement on one side and twelve cells for protective custody on the other side. The cells are small, the furniture minimal, the beds permanently attached to cement floors, and inmates locked down twenty-three hours a day. Fiske, on the other hand, has terrazzo floors, marble showers, and lovely hand-hammered down-spouts, all vestiges of another age when such grandeur could have been bought at ordinary prices. But one does still wonder why a place meant for special punishment was made quite so fine.

I lived at Fiske for three years. Sitting on my bed where I read and wrote and knitted and sewed, I could always see Bettye's name. It distracted me sometimes. It was in the putty outside the window, a hard place to reach because of the metal bars every five inches. But out there the matron wouldn't notice it and add "defacing state property" to Bettye's list of other sins. Only another inmate would notice it. Only another inmate would wonder who Bettye was.

I'll never know about Bettye, what sent her here, what made her cry, whether she became a useful citizen when she left. But I do know about Alba, who is here now as a woman of fifty-five and was also here at seventeen when the place was still a reformatory. She did time at Fiske then because a matron approached her as though she were going to hit her with a large bunch of keys and Alba grabbed her wrist. Touching matrons then was like touching a corrections officer today. Whatever the circumstances you just don't do it. When you do, it's listed as assault and you go to SHU.

Alba was placed in one of four small rooms at Fiske on the ground floor, with no window to the sky, only a small window looking out on a brick wall a few feet away. The wall encloses a tiny courtyard covered over with a heavy iron grating. The only view of the sky is

20

straight up. Walking in tiny circles in the court was her only outdoor exercise and fresh air for two months. As irony would have it, those four tiny rooms today are called "the garden apartments" at Fiske and much sought after by all of the women but me. I prayed never to be housed in one of them, and since we drew lots for rooms and my number was eighteen, and those four tiny rooms were the first ones chosen, I was saved. Views of the sky are not a high priority item in here, which is one of its many mysteries to me.

When Alba was finally released from the reformatory she stayed out of trouble for twenty-four years, during which time she built up a respectable small business. When released she had been listed as an "expert seamstress" on the industrial sewing machine. "I could even make very good buttonholes." She reported for work in one of New York's many sweatshops with her application clearly marked "convict." The man in charge, as was probably his custom with many of the young girls who reported there from the reformatory, made a pass. Alba walked out and never went back. As she walked along Madison Avenue, she saw a "help wanted" sign in a pet store, went in, got the job and worked there for seven years learning everything the owner had to teach about pet care and grooming. "I can even cut their nails and clean their teeth." Eventually she moved to suburbia and set herself up in business. She prospered for twenty-four years.

I asked her, "Which do you think was the better run place, the reformatory or the prison? Which did the most for you?" "The reformatory, no question," she said. "But then why did you come back?" I asked. "Because I'm a lesbian, Jean. I went to trial, and I think I'd have been acquitted until the D.A., knowing the answer, asked me if I was a lesbian. From that moment on the jury knew all they wanted to know. They thought a lesbian was capable of anything. My lifestyle brought me here." That's the way Alba put it.

There's another near neighbor of mine in here, Connie, who came to the reformatory as a kid of sixteen at the behest of her parents who found her incorrigible. Now, twenty-seven years later, she's here at the prison on a drug charge.

Alba and Connie provided my first history lesson about Bedford Hills Correctional Facility. It didn't jibe with what we had been told by administration about Fiske Cottage when we moved there. "It used to be part of the old Rockefeller estate," they told us. "Fiske was Mr. Rockefeller's private hunting lodge." It doesn't look like a hunting lodge from the outside, and inside Mr. Rockefeller's guests would have to have shared one bathtub and one toilet with nine other guests. That didn't trouble anyone but me, the theory being, I guess, that you rough it when you go hunting.

The name of Rockefeller came up more than once. Somehow, in myth or in fact, he had touched this place. I wondered how and why. As an old history teacher I found the bits and pieces of information I had come upon quite by accident made for an incomplete and thoroughly unsatisfactory picture of the place where I live and work. Is it a reflection of what it had been when Bettye was here, I wondered? Is it better today because it has been here in some form for a long time? Has it acquired the wisdom of age, or just grown older? Has it incorporated into its daily policies the lessons we've learned about our own humanness? I began to search for answers.

One

"You shoulda known me when I was a little black princess."

"I was a little black princess, too, a beautiful little black princess."

We constantly hear about and observe the remarkable changes in our lives that have been wrought in the past fifty years. I still have an old oil lamp that my mother used as a young student. I can remember chamber pots under the big beds at my grandmother's house. No one I knew had a television set until after I was married and my son David was born. Computers once filled whole rooms to do the work that a chip the size of your fingernail can do today. Doctors can perform medical magic on people once doomed to die. We've even taken a trip to the moon. Each one is a separate marvel. Each one leaves us wondering: Where do people fit in? Have they changed enough to fit the hardware? Or should they have to?

I've lived through three revolutions in my life. The first one Mr. Roosevelt brought about by guess and by God during the thirties, improvising as he went along, and probably having little understanding of the breadth of his actions on the years that were to follow. I can remember sitting on the stair landing when my mother and father came home from an election night party in 1936. Roosevelt had just been reelected for the first time. "It's the end of a way of life, Jean," my father said. "Our world will never be the same again. My God, where do all those Democrats come from?" We sat wide-eyed and silent as he walked upstairs to bed.

The 1960s brought another revolution. David Harris, my older son, went to Woodstock, and that was its beginning for me. That nice rural atmosphere for young people to sit out under the stars and listen to music helped usher out the set of values I had found logical and comfortable for a lifetime and ushered in an ethos of anything goes, to the accompaniment of sounds and noises I still find difficult to acknowledge as music.

The third revolution I have watched from prison, sitting at the bottom of the stairs looking up, as steel mills have closed down (remember the old saying, "as steel goes so goes the nation"?), thousands of people have lost high-paying jobs with only low-paying ones to turn to, and a large slice of our once smug monopoly on car production has gone to the countries we defeated in the Second World War: Japan, Germany and Italy. Private fortunes in this country now exceed three billion dollars, while a larger proportion of our children than ever before are living in poverty. Fifty-five percent of our urban minority children drop out of school without graduating, without even learning to read. According to the United States Justice Department, our prison population has increased by 50 percent in the past five years, and a house my husband and I built as young marrieds for $21,000 I could buy back today for over $200,000. Now I am the one to tell my children, "It's the end of an era, David." "Our lives will never be the same again, Jim."

But it isn't the end of the world. It's time, as Melville put it, "to create new kinds of social enrichment." The lives of the women I live with might be a good place to start. How much do we know today about incarcerated women that we didn't know eighty-seven years ago? How did we help women crawl out of the holes they had dug for themselves then? How much do we help them today to survive "on the outside"? If we've grown so smart, why are more women per hundred thousand being arrested today than ever before in our history? Why are they going to prison faster than men are? Has baby really come a long way, I ask myself, or has she just been following an ever winding path between point A and point B for a long time?

A glimpse into cell block 112A may give you some idea of what life is like for the eight hundred women presently incarcerated here. For example, take this morning.

Ellen is sitting on a chair outside of Rosie's cell. She has turned her face away so I can't see her crying. I've put on my glasses and pretended to read so she can't see that I am crying, too. It's a fairly normal day here, the usual tragedy all around, some people caring, some people totally unconcerned. As Lovey always says, "I come here to do my time, and I don't give a shit about nobody else."

Ellen cares, and so do I. We might be better off if we didn't. Caring takes a heavy toll in here, there's so much to care about. And the most unsettling thing of all is that sometimes you aren't absolutely sure if the strong thing you feel is love or anger.

There are thirty cells on my corridor. I've lived here since I was removed, most unceremoniously yet with much fanfare, from the prison honor cottage. I had been on probation most of the time I was there. Of the two reasons given in writing for my being on probation, the first one was denied by the C.O. who said it hadn't happened. The second one read, "Jean Harris thinks she is better than other people." I'm not sure what part of the Correctional Law of New York State that violates, but that's the reason I was given for serving two years on probation. What did me in at the end was a five-inch bud vase made in the arts and crafts class here and given to me by one of the other prisoners for Christmas. The C.O. whose evaluation had put me on probation delivered the coup de grâce. "It's your own fault," she said. "You brought this on yourself. If you'd kept the vase in the kitchen, it would have been all right."

"I wish I knew the words," I told her grandly, "to express the depth of my contempt for you," and walked upstairs to pack. This piece of history was quickly sent out to the media by someone in Albany who announced, "Mrs. Harris cursed the C.O." To her, it may have sounded like one, and I certainly intended it as one, so I packed my worldly goods, and, like Brer Rabbit, headed for the briar patch. Like Brer Rabbit, too, I discovered it was where I belonged if I was ever to know what this prison is truly like. It is unpleasant in the extreme, but it is real, oh so real.

Rosie is crying now, too. Tears are streaming down her wide black face. She is fifty-two but she thinks she is twelve years old again and that Connie is her mother. She's sobbing now, "Please don't send me to Bellevue. Please don't let them put the jacket on me. It burns my arms, Mommy. . . . What did I do, Mommy? What did I do to make you mad at me? What did I do?"

We've moved her out of the hall and into her cell and onto the mattress which sits on the floor because she has fallen out of bed so many times at the violent start of one of her grand mal seizures. Ten percent of the women on my floor have seizures, but none like Rosie's. In addition she has asthma, diabetes and glaucoma. She has spent years of her life in and out of hospitals and mental institutions. She has had a surfeit of prescription drugs and shock treatments. Now she slips more and more into the seizures and loses track of where she is. As her next-door neighbor, I can usually tell when she is going to be ill. Sometimes she calls "Jean" in a frightened voice, knowing it's about to happen and I try to get some help if we're locked in. Other times I know she has started when I hear the low, guttural sounds she makes and the choking on phlegm and things being knocked to the floor. At such times, she throws her large body about like a dog shaking a rag doll, arms and legs kicking and flailing about, mouth foaming.

Connie is in her cell now trying to get her to sleep. Rosie is lying on her side under the covers and Connie is lying almost on top of her, cradling her as best she can in her arms. It is a sight too sad to see. It is a sight too beautiful to miss. It is Mary and Child on a prison cell floor. There are no lambs today, only cockroaches to play the role.

With the promise that "Mommy's going to take you home," Rosie is now on her way down to the medical building, clinging like a child to Ellen on one side and Connie on the other. The C.O. says, "Don't forget your ID," and tries to hand it to her. She shrinks back from him. She has no idea what an ID is or why a stranger is trying to put the thing into her hand. Obviously not too much enlightenment has brightened Rosie's life. The only big difference for her over the years is that as a child she was kept in mental hospitals, and today, now that she is larger and potentially more dangerous, she is kept in prison.

Regina, another inmate who has frequent epileptic seizures too, had a fight with her prison lover last week, who told her in graphic terms to "get lost." Regina ran back to her cell friendless and sobbing deep convulsive sobs. Then she grew quiet while she tried to hang herself. She was found in time and taken to

Marcy for the criminally insane. She'll be back in a few days.

Loretta, who was born a male and is now female, is often in lock. Her many different frustrations roil about in her brain. She lives in a constant state of anger at the world, right on the edge of a screaming, screeching tantrum. She is often mocked by the other women, and even some who try to help her are often hard to distinguish from the mockers. "Jesus Christ, Loretta! Go back and comb yer fuckin' hair. You look like shit. A woman ain't supposed to go around lookin' like that." On the few occasions when she ventures into stockings and heels she looks from the back for all the world like Tony Curtis running along beside the train in *Some Like It Hot*. Someone always jeers.

The C.O.s drive her crazy and the feelings are mutual. She bares her teeth at them almost like an angry dog. Three days ago, the anger exploded again and Loretta decided to set her cell on fire, a highly flammable area since she rarely clears anything out of it. Arson is a serious offense so she will be in lock for ten days or so. She has printed a sign for her door which reads, "I hope all of my enemies get Cancer and rot." She has also announced that she is on a hunger strike, "until I get satisfaction." What "satisfaction" will consist of is as much a mystery to her as to me.

Olga is a pretty, almost exotic looking young woman whose brain is now pickled in drugs. There are also whispered tales of incest. What condition her mind was in when she started out I don't know. There are moments when one gets the feeling she was once quite normal. Saturday she walked out to the recreation room after giving herself "a scalp treatment." She had mixed a concoction of cigarette ashes, coffee grounds and feces and rubbed it over every part of her scalp. It had begun to dry in long pointed spikes, looking like what might have been Dante's version of the Statue of Liberty. One of the inmates, far braver than I, took

28

her into the shower and washed her hair, and then for a few days she was taken to Satellite, an area in the prison for serious mental cases.

Renee got a message to call a certain number that she wasn't familiar with. I was waiting for one of the two phones, too, but I'm not as patient as she. I think something told her the message was one she didn't want to hear, and it could wait. We were each at one of the phones when she heard, "Your baby burned to death this morning in a house fire." He was nine months old. She had asked to be allowed to keep the baby here for its first year, but she had tried to commit suicide while she was at Rikers Island and the doctors felt she was not stable enough to live on a floor with twenty-six other mothers and babies. She made not a sound. I didn't know until later about the baby. Her manner reminds me of my pictures of a Masai chief. She is tall and straight and quiet and dignified. She hung up the phone, walked quietly to her cell, and asked the C.O. to lock her in.

When I heard about the baby, I wrote her a note, adding "If there is anything I can do for you, please let me know," and slipped it under the door of her cell. The day after the baby's funeral, which she was allowed to attend, she slipped this under my door:

Dear Mrs. Harris,

I haven't money in my commissary fund for these and I need two bars of toilet soap, some laundry soap and Vaseline. And really would like some Oreo cookies, but just get what you can. Thank you very much.

I don't know the answers to many of the problems in here, but one thing I know for sure: When your baby burns to death, by God you deserve an Oreo cookie. I have learned in here how much easier it is to give than to receive. It is a privilege few of these women enjoy,

29

and it is one of the reasons they are not schooled in gratitude.

It's May as I write this. Martha was supposed to go home on February fifteenth, but she is to be deported to Colombia where her family lives, and the people in charge of such things here don't seem to know the proper procedures to follow. Consequently, she is still here. The prison administration blames the Immigration Department, and the Immigration Department says it was all mishandled by the prison. Whatever it was, Martha and her children are the victims. Her case is further complicated by the fact that one of her two children was born in Colombia, and one was born in the United States. They have been in foster care while Martha was here. Now the social worker handling their case is suggesting that the American-born child should stay behind when mother and brother go to Colombia. Martha is down to ninety-five pounds, and is totally confused by what little English she can understand, as are all the bureaucrats who talk to her.

Loda runs up to me and tells me excitedly that she will soon be going home. Her lawyer told her that if she would sell her home and give him $15,000 he could get her out. At least that's what she thinks he said, but she often fails to understand. She sometimes stares at you with dead eyes. From time to time she goes into what seems a catatonic state and seems totally unaware of anyone or anything. She has now sold the house for what little it was worth, and her mother and three youngest children have moved twice since then. Her oldest daughter is "on the street" and her oldest son tried to commit suicide. The lawyer has been paid his $15,000; the appeal is in, and now as far as Loda is concerned, it's just a matter of weeks before she will be out.

I'm told Loda killed her husband by bashing him over the head with a baseball bat. Carmen tells the story of sitting at a table in the visiting room with her and her mother one day. The mother was angry and turned on her saying, "You got what you deserved. He was a good man." Carmen said, "I felt bad for Loda. She was crying." "What did you do?" I asked. "I said to her mother, 'Listen, nobody's perfect.' "

Nothing has prepared Loda for the fact that she will almost surely lose her appeal. She will not understand. She will feel cheated and deceived. She will do something violent. She has already tried suicide. The saddest part of her story lies ahead.

Jo Jo has AIDS and has been moved to another floor to break up her love affair with Jonsie. Vickie has terminal cancer. She has served nine years, and Sister Elaine, New York State Senator Israel Ruiz and others are trying to get her a medical discharge so that she can die at home. To date, all appeals have been denied although the doctor has written to Albany saying she has three months to live and adding that the care she has had in prison has from all indications shortened her life. She said to me yesterday, "I can handle it all, Jean, except the thought of dying in prison. That's the worst." In the meantime, the kindnesses to her from inmates on the floor is a heartwarming thing to see.

Maria spends hours with her, gently rubbing her back, talking to her in soothing terms, "I take care of you, Mommy. You need something, I get it for you." Kathy, who lives next door, ties a string of yarn between their cells in such a way that Vickie can waken her in the night if she needs help. Ellen cooks her favorite Italian food, and urges her to eat to keep up her strength. Others, returning from the visiting room with packages from home, bring something special to her room — fresh berries, a garden tomato, a new magazine. Others, with nothing to give, come to her room to sit for a little while, sharing the gossip of the floor. It frightens her to be alone, and she is left alone only when we are all locked in our cells. Even a few of the

31

most disturbed women try to soothe her pain with kindness.

Many women here are comfortable with sorrow. It's an old member of the family, and they greet it as one would. Good fortune is quite another thing. It is a stranger, and they greet it as an alien, especially if they see it in someone else's cell. If you've won an appeal, beware. There are women who have themselves placed in protective custody until they leave, so no one can spoil their departure, not an inmate, not an officer.

One's mortality is a subject often pondered by prisoners. I think of the man on the mental ward at Coxsackie Men's Prison who ran up to Sister Elaine while she was visiting there one day. "You're a Sister, right?" "Yes, I am." "So you know a lot about dead people, right?" "Well, I try to comfort people when a loved one dies." "Well, Charlie told me before they put ya in the box they put the handcuffs on ya. Jesus! I don't wanta go in the box in handcuffs!" But that was another day and another prison.

Death and tragedy are as old as the world and come to all of us; it's just that here in prison they seem to be so crowded into one small space. "Why does today have to be so bad? Yesterday was bad enough for the whole week." Yet when prisons first came to this country they were looked upon as a great step forward in the human march toward decency and compassion. We congratulated ourselves for building them.

Obviously what we accept today should not be judged in the light of yesterday's values. The word *values* is the stumbling block. Prisons, like schools, do not create values; they mirror them, something the average citizen is not comfortable being told. They are the two institutions we like to think will make everything better, and we get very cross when they don't. And the crosser we get the more determined we become to keep doing the same things over and over again, "until we get it right." "Back to basics" is the cry of the educational experts. "Lock 'em up and throw away the key," is the penal equivalent. We even have a congressman who endorses a new Devil's Island, "somewhere off the coast of Alaska." Where do the Connies and Rosies and Lodas of Bedford fit in? How do they ride the tides of history? Are they buffeted about less today because we know how to fly to the moon? The only way to find out is to go back and take a look.

Two

A society can be judged by what goes on in its prisons.

DOSTOEVSKY

To begin to probe into the history of this prison might be difficult for anyone, but it is especially difficult if one is an inmate. There are plenty of records of the early years but by now they are largely preserved in archives and cannot be sent out. One must go to the libraries where they are. Later, more recent records are, I'm told, wrapped in bureaucracy and not easy for anyone to reach.

If you are a prisoner like me who has already publicly stated that things are not quite to your liking here, the few questions you do ask often elicit a nervous, "Whatta ya wanta know for?" In fact, the only direct question that I put to staff members elicited an answer that canceled all the rest. I asked, "How many acres of property are there to this facility?" and I certainly asked it in total innocence. I knew that the facility had started out on 107½ acres, and I had read that it later bought 91 more. I had even read somewhere what the total acreage was, but I hadn't written it down and I couldn't remember where I had seen it. I can't remember now why I even thought it mattered.

I asked several staff members who shrugged that they didn't know, and finally I asked one of the staff secretaries. "I don't know," she said, "but I'm sure I can find out." She is a particularly kind and thoughtful lady, and the last person I would want to cause any trouble. Next time I saw her, she was visibly shaken. "I was told that under no condition, at any time, ever, is anyone to tell Jean Harris the acreage of this facility." "Why?" I asked. "I don't really understand why," she said, "but it has something to do with if anyone plans an escape by helicopter it would be a great help to them to know the total acreage." It was also suggested that asking or answering questions for inmates could lead to loss of job.

I remain, in spite of giving it earnest consideration, totally mystified as to how a helicopter escape from this prison or any prison would be facilitated by knowing the facility's acreage. When you land it first, what matters is being on the inside of the tall fences, and when you land it next it is important to be on the outside of the tall fences. However, the whole thing is best forgotten. I have been given charge sheets for just about everything else in here, including "inciting a riot," and "stealing a bushel of blueberries," but aiding and abetting prison escapes I want no part of. Hence, you will never find out from me how many acres there are at Bedford Hills Correctional Facility. Even if I knew I wouldn't tell.

Curiosity, though I've already said I'm glad I have some, is not the royal road to trust or popularity with the gang on a prison campus, keeper and kept alike. In fact, the first serious rule you learn in prison (unlike, "Never use obscene language," which no one takes seriously), is "Never ask questions." For example, when some friendly soul slips you some butter and two fresh eggs, never ask, "Where'd you get them?" When someone who knows practically everything tells you which one of the women the tall C.O. on cell block X is having sex with in the dining room after it's closed for the night, never ask, "How do you know?" And when they tell you to whom which one of the captains gave a ruby ring last Christmas, act as though you already knew. All of which may explain in part why there will be no footnotes in this book, something that saddens me because I am a consummate reader of footnotes. I even check *ibid.*

I had heard through the prison grapevine that the place I needed to get to was the basement of the prison administration building. "It's full of old records." The only thing I knew for sure was down there was the Children's Center's big plastic Christmas tree. I tried to figure out how I could help fetch the Christmas tree when the right time came, but I was assured, "Inmates never go down there." Then someone told me, "There's nothing down there anymore. It all went up to Albany." I still don't know what's down there. All I do know is, I'm not about to find out.

It was good friends with a little historical curiosity of their own, who finally opened some doors for me — library doors, and doors to newspaper archives — and started me on my historical way. I had been collecting reports and studies of women's prisons in general since I arrived here in the spring of 1981. Now, with the bibliographies from those studies to start with I began making lists and writing people. Rosa Paladino, the prison librarian was very helpful and tracked down two particularly important books, one published in 1912, another in 1923. Charlie and Gay Lord made several trips to the Vassar library for me and even copied some articles in longhand when they couldn't be photocopied. Like Gay, Katherine Davis, who was the first superintendent of the original facility here, was a Vassar graduate and a member of its Board of Trustees, so

36

its library proved a good place to begin. Davis had earned her Ph.D. at the University of Chicago, and it too proved to have some colorful articles about her in old university magazines.

Sue Cullman got for me printouts of every *New York Times* article about the reformatory, and later the prison from 1919 on. Joan Devereaux, head of volunteers here, had a few old and interesting publications, what little there is here in the way of archives. I have since been making copies of whatever I find and making a set for the prison library. The Westchester Historical Society kindly shared what information it had, as did the Elizabeth Fry Society of Canada, and the Corrections Association of New York provided many of its excellent reports. It is hardly what one could call learned research, flotsam and jetsam at best, but then we who are imprisoned here, and have been over the years, are flotsam and jetsam, too, so perhaps this is the most logical way to learn about us.

Historically, until the last few years, there has been so little thought given to women who broke the law that their early history takes little time to cover. There have been three general attitudes toward such women since we ratified our Constitution. There is, of course, no single moment when one attitude replaced another. They overlapped and created strong social tensions in some circles. Until somewhere in the late 1860s, just after the Civil War, there was one word to describe a female lawbreaker. She was "depraved." A man who broke the law was just being his normal, rough, tough aggressive self. He had broken the law of man, but he had not broken any laws of nature that required him to be other than he was being. Not so with women. God had created a woman to be passive and pure, loving and fertile, obedient and submissive. When she committed a crime she had not only offended society, she had offended God. The "Cult of True Womanhood" had been violated. There was no hope for her redemption. There was no punishment too coarse for her. And her crimes consisted of anything from nagging to gossiping to adultery to murder. Even pouting could get her into trouble.

Nathaniel Hawthorne's book *The Scarlet Letter*, published in 1850, was a literary expression of the "Cult of True Womanhood." I think of Hester Prynne sometimes when I watch Marie, a beautiful mother in here. Her baby girl was born just before she was sent to prison for fifteen years to life for a nonviolent first offense. She fought to keep the baby with her in jail, won and brought it with her to Bedford where young Julia stayed until her first birthday. We watched her learn to crawl and walk on the bright blue carpet in the Children's Center. She is her mother's reason for living, and every day is a new struggle to be sure she is safe and happy and not too far away. When Hester is told that her daughter Pearl will be taken from her she responds, "God gave me the child! . . . He gave her, in requital of all things else, which ye had taken from me. She is my happiness! Pearl punishes me too! See ye not, she is the scarlet letter, only capable of being loved, and so endowed with a million-fold the power of retribution for my sin? Ye shall not take her!" I don't know what part *The Scarlet Letter* played in the strong sympathies for women prisoners who grew up among feminists and social reformers, but their timing is similar, and I imagine they touched.

From approximately 1870 to 1930, we went through the reformatory stage, when the public permitted itself to be convinced that quite the opposite of what we had once preached was true. It was now the female wrongdoer who could be reformed and made new again, not the male. Penitentiaries had been built for men. Reformatories would now be built for women. Furthermore, to send a woman or girl to the reformatory was not punishment, she was told. It was an expression of the public's parental concern for her. Because of that kindly concern it was not uncommon for a woman to spend many more months imprisoned than did a man who had committed the same offense.

By the 1930s what had started out as reformatories had become essentially prisons for women. There was now less sisterhood and more authority practiced. Whatever the public's attitude toward women, they were now going to get what some of them thought they wanted, namely, the same treatment as men, or as close as anyone could get to it. Gender specific began to slide toward gender neutral and the dichotomy of the two is still a bone of contention among feminists of many persuasions.

From everything I can observe and read there is still a world of difference between a men's and women's prison, at least in the State of New York. Whether that's good, bad, wise or unwise, fair or unfair are questions we are presently wrestling with. There are occasional administrators who come here briefly from a men's prison who want to see us far more regimented than we are and who snipe at small things that are important to the women, "No more jewelry to be worn in the visiting room." "No more sitting next to a friend in the dining room — not there — fill up that table before you go to another one." "No more this — no more that" — the little things that breathe some sense of humanness into a day disappear one by one. I still know of no women's prison where inmates must march two by two to meals with cans of mace set up along the way at the ready in case someone gets violent. This is, I'm told, commonplace at Sing Sing and Attica and other state prisons for men. I know of no men's prisons, on the other hand, where inmates flirt outrageously with staff members and tell them, "You're cute, honey. Ya look a little like Dennis the Menace. I'd like to take you home for a pet."

From a woman depraved, to a woman wronged, to a woman who now says she wants to be treated equally with men, we've spanned two hundred years, and we're more ambivalent today than we ever were. We are loathe to or just unable to define what is a man and what is a woman and what we want our prisons to accomplish for both. If there is a national prison philosophy, it is a well-kept secret. If anybody has decided what everyone else's role is, that's restricted material, too.

While New York was still a colony, it dealt with criminals harshly, as did all other colonies. It tortured, flogged, burned, branded, used the ducking stool and pillory on men and women alike. And every punishment was inflicted publicly in an atmosphere not unlike a county fair. There were sixteen different crimes punishable by death in the State of New York, while the Miracle of Philadelphia was being acted out and the Constitution was being born.

Happily, in 1796, the death penalty in New York was abolished for all crimes except murder and treason. Soon thereafter, the first city jail in New York was built in what is now Greenwich Village and named Newgate after Newgate Gaol in London.

The Quakers in Philadelphia introduced the concept of penitentiaries to the new country almost from its beginning, with the idea that if wrongdoers were isolated from society, and even from one another, they would have the time and silence needed to study the bible and repent their sins. The pendulum swung from the most public to the most private possible infliction of punishment.

The first warden of New York's Newgate Jail in a public address announced proudly, "This prison will become a model for other prisons which may become necessary in our extensive country, and will reflect lasting honors on the State of New York." The myth that prisons and honor are in any way associated is as old as our country.

When Newgate opened, burglary, forgery and stealing from the church "on a regular basis," were all punishable by life imprisonment. Inmates lived eight to a cell (then called "apartments") which measured twelve feet by eight feet, with one slop bucket for all. They worked from 5:00 A.M. to 7:00 P.M. daily. Women were tossed into the same "apartments" as men, in fact, men, women, children, syphilitic babies, sick and well, sane and insane, were all together. It was not uncommon for a woman to have to give herself sexually in order to get her daily food. Obviously, that's no longer required, but I'm told it's still one way to get a really good meal. Prison clothes were not provided, prisoners lived in filth, in unbearable heat and unbearable cold, and death from all the hazards was common. By 1827, because of what was described as "universal riots and debauchery" in Philadelphia, men and women were finally separated into their own prison areas. In New York City, Newgate continued to be little more than a public brothel.

But grim as it was, Newgate did nothing to deter crime. Before he knew it, the Governor of New York had to start pardoning one group of wrongdoers to make way for another group. Today's media notwithstanding, overcrowding has been a problem in our prisons since the first ones were built early in the nineteenth century. Prisons are a self-fulfilling prophecy. They were then. They are now. It's logistically impossible ever to build enough prisons, because by their very existence they will be filled. But two hundred years of this repetitive story have still not convinced many citizens that prisons do not deter crime.

In 1816 the first large state penitentiary in America was built in Auburn, New York, and named after the town. Its first warden, William Britton, had been one of the carpenters on the job, and the proud Board pointed out in its first report how clever it had been to get both a warden and a carpenter for the price of one—$1,800 per year.

Like Newgate, Auburn started out with eight to ten prisoners in an apartment, but they soon proved to be schools for crime, and as new buildings were added single cells were built, for men, not for women. The single cells measured seven feet long and three and one half feet wide. When a large man sat on the side of his bed, his knees bumped into a wall.

Like Newgate's first warden, many people considered the great fortresslike buildings at Auburn to be a giant humanitarian step forward, since fewer wrongdoers would now be hanged. Others considered it an economic breakthrough for the new country, which needed a large labor supply. Prisons would save and train "needed laborers so even our least able would do useful work."

Whatever their original purpose, prisons soon deteriorated into what they are essentially today: human warehouses. Women were and still are more constrained by nature and upbringing than men, and for a long time were a negligible part of the prison count. Even today, they are only about 5 percent of it, but five percent of five hundred thousand state prisoners is a lot. Women are closer to 10 percent of those who go to jail in the course of a year.

The solitary confinement of Quaker prisons forbade any inmates to speak, ever. They spent their days and nights alone in their cells in absolute silence. Instead of repenting, some went mad.

To remove some of the harshness of the Quaker "solitary system," Auburn, though it enforced absolute silence at all times, allowed contact with other prisoners during work assignments. It was still an incredibly harsh atmosphere, with beatings by the guards commonplace. However, the "Auburn system" as it was called—alone at night, working in groups by day, and silence at all times—became widely known and widely copied all over the country.

Auburn was also advanced in that it separated the sexes right from the start. The men were put into cells and the women were sent to a single attic room over the prison kitchen. There was no matron to supervise them, food came in once a day, and the head of the kitchen was called in case of an emergency to break up fights and to "counsel."

After a young woman five months pregnant died from a beating, a matron was finally hired, but even after this the prison chaplain wrote, "to be a male convict in this prison would be quite tolerable, but to be a female convict for any protracted period of time would be worse than death." By the late 1830s, the women were finally moved into cells, thus gaining some privacy, as well as a great deal more regimentation.

Baltimore claims credit for being the first city to bring female supervision to women prisoners in 1822 in the form of matrons. It was the 1880s before they came to New York City. Until then, the women, many imprisoned for prostitution, were even given body searches by men. "Justice" was often more corrupt than the prostitutes it punished. I am not persuaded that, minus the body searches, the same is not true today and the end product now, as then, is a hardened woman. Two female C.O.s from Rikers Island recently spent a few nights in Bedford's SHU after it was discovered they were running a prostitution ring at Rikers. We're told they've now been moved to a federal prison.

The Inspectors of Prisons said of the women at Auburn, "Crowded as these females are, about thirty in number in a single room of small dimensions and very imperfect ventilation, in the fourth story of the south wing, they are obliged to remain day and night in an atmosphere absolutely nauseating to a visitor. Their condition is truly wretched as regards health and government, and with respect to prospect of reformation, utterly hopeless."

By 1828, Newgate Jail in New York City was closed down. The men went to the newly completed prison in Ossining, soon to be notorious as Sing Sing, on the Hudson River — or "up the river" as the movies taught us. There wasn't any state prison for women at the time, so the women from Newgate went to a county prison, Bellevue, where the state contracted to pay $100 a year per woman for maintenance. Today that wouldn't pay for two days. Once again the women were herded into a large common room, without supervision, their days spent washing and sewing for New York City's male convicts. Sing Sing's inspectors came as required, as infrequently as possible, and found each time the women's food inadequate, their living quarters unsanitary, and classifications impossible: felons, misdemeanants, young, old, sick, well, sane, and insane still all together. There they remained for nine years, until a women's prison at Sing Sing, named Mt. Pleasant after the hill in back of the men's facility, was built, and then only because Bellevue refused to take any more state prisoners. According to a report issued by the New York State Department of Corrections, money for the women's prison was to be paid for "out of convict earnings," which probably meant convicts did all the work and no one was paid. In June 1839, Mt. Pleasant was completed and all female felons in New York State henceforth were to be sent directly there by the courts. The building contained eighty-one cells, in tiers like the men's.

Treatment for the women was as rough as that for the men and could include bread and water diets for long periods of time, straightjacketing, solitary confinement, and hosing down until close to drowning. Of the above only solitary confinement and the occasional use of fire hoses are used at Bedford Hills today. The water treatment, or "gag" as it was called, was dangerous and terrifying. Dorothea Dix called it "shocking and extremely objectionable." A Sing Sing inspector explained that the "gag" was used occasionally on the men but it was only on the females that it was "absolutely necessary."

Within four years, 1843, the place was overcrowded and the women were rebellious. Though it had a room called "the nursery," the care available for five infants born there was horrendous. "The place is bedlam and the early death of the child is inevitable." The governor pardoned two of the young mothers, but one baby died before the mother left. The other baby lived and is recorded as "the only instance of a child born in a prison up to that time who had gone out alive."

A matron was brought in to oversee the women, but all ultimate decisions were made by the male head of Sing Sing. One lady whose name bears remembering in the history of women's prisons is that of Eliza Farnham. As a matron, she brought some semblance of civility into the women's lives at Mt. Pleasant, encouraging volunteers from outside to come and visit them, bringing in flowers, books and music, and permitting the women to talk to one another while they worked, though the men were still held to complete silence. This caused considerable dissension. When Farnham left, the silence rule returned. Later, it was continued for the women at Auburn into the twentieth century.

As people with good ideas often are, Farnham was widely criticized and publicly attacked. Among the most vocal of her critics was Sing Sing's chaplain. "She has been letting those women read novels." She finally resigned in 1847. From the standpoint of good penology, for the rest of its existence the history of Mt. Pleasant was downhill all the way.

By 1865 it had more than twice as many inmates as it had single cells. In 1877, Mt. Pleasant was finally closed and women again had to be farmed out to county prisons. In 1892, what had been Matteawan State Hospital for Insane Men became the women's prison at Auburn and so it remained, with all the charm the name implied, until it went out of existence in 1933 and all the state's female felons were moved here to Bedford Hills.

Three

Some who administered male prisons suggested it would be better to send a woman to a brothel than to jail, that way she could at least run from corruption.

ESTELLE B. FREEDMAN,
Their Sisters' Keepers

During the Civil War, as during the First and Second World Wars, the number of women's convictions rose faster than men's. Men who might have gone to prisons now went to war instead. "Our boys" needed protection from "loose women" and the diseases they spread. "Crimes against chastity" brought the largest numbers of women to prison during the war years. They might include, "lewd and lascivious carriage, idle and disorderly conduct, vagrancy, fornication and adultery." Once convicted, the women were social pariahs. Even men convicted of the same crime as a woman looked down on her. The lines between "good" and "bad" were starkly drawn. But as the number of female inmates grew, the number of middle-class women concerned about them grew, too.

While Philadelphia Quaker women were the first

Americans to concern themselves with imprisoned women, by 1840, Protestant missionary women were visiting women in the New York City Tombs, and pressing for a separate facility for them. They finally got it, just eighty-eight years later, in 1932. It was called the New York House of Detention. Catholic and Jewish women started later to visit prisons, but soon caught up with the others in their concerns and contributions to the prison reform movement.

The Civil War helped bring about a small change for the better in the public's view of middle-class women. They had served as charity workers, nurses, clerks, couriers in the midst of battle. They had proved their competency and some of them wanted now to continue their work not as volunteers, but as professionals. It was women who did much of the tracing and aiding of war widows and their dependents. As they continued their prison work, they found themselves in a stronger position to be heard and to push for separate prisons for women.

The year was 1870, when the woman depraved began a metamorphosis into the woman wronged, the woman led astray, the woman "who is more to be pitied than censured." It was also the year that a national convention of penologists and reformers met in Cincinnati, Ohio, and formally endorsed the idea of creating separate, treatment-oriented prisons for women. The Woman's House of Shelter had been established two years earlier as part of the Detroit House of Corrections and served briefly as a role model. It held thirty inmates who lived together, "family style." A matron was hired there to create "a family atmosphere" and to lift the intellectual and the moral and the skill levels of the inmates: A Detroit school teacher served as the matron. It also endorsed indeterminate sentencing since no one could say exactly how long reformations would take. Unfortunately, the Shelter was soon closed to women when more room was needed for men. The concept of indeterminate sentencing for women became popular, however, in part because with such sentences mental defectives could be kept out of the sexual market until their child-bearing days were over.

The Industrial Revolution played a role in the spread of women's concern for causes outside the home. During the colonial period and the settlement of the West, it was pointless to decide whether the man or the woman played the more important role in family survival. Shared work, hard physical labor held the family together and few men could be so foolish as to say the woman's contribution was less than his. Marriage was a basic economic necessity and so were children, to share the burdens and take over when parents had worn themselves out. In colonial times a four-year-old could weed, spin, sew, feed the animals, mind the baby, knit and embroider.

With the rise of factories women stopped spinning thread, weaving cloth, sewing the family clothes, making soap and candles and buttons and butter and began to buy them ready-made. With canned food, an icebox and a carpet sweeper, she was relieved of further drudgery. All the energy had to go somewhere so it went to causes. Women became concerned about things they had never had time to worry about before.

The roots of feminism lie deep within the prison reform movement, and some of the earliest glimmers of it were in the eyes of a little English Quaker woman named Elizabeth Fry, who came from a deeply religious and antislavery family. An abolitionist father can be found at the hearthside of many early feminists. They learned at their father's knee about concern for the downtrodden, and later they learned they were downtrodden, too.

Visiting prisons was not an unusual activity for Quaker ladies when Elizabeth Fry first entered London's Newgate Gaol in 1813. But when she saw the abject wretchedness there, women and children, barely clothed, hungry, cold, ill-used in every way, she made up her mind she was going to do everything in her power to relieve the horrors she saw. She had arrived with her bible tucked under her arm, bent on proselytizing and reforming, and quickly realized that food, clothing and protection from those who preyed on the weak must be provided, too. Over the next ten years, she developed a set of principles by which prisons for women should be run and prisoners treated. First among them was that women prisoners should be superintended by women in their own institutions.

Mrs. Fry's influence in England was broad during the early years of her work but by 1825, it had begun to wane—and by 1835, some of the changes she had helped bring about were being rescinded as "too soft." Reverend Sydney Smith, then a canon of St. Paul's, wrote:

> There must be no visiting of friends—no education but religious education—no freedom of diet—no weavers' looms or carpenters' benches. There must be a great deal of solitude, coarse food, a dress of shame, hard, incessant, irksome external labour; a planned and regulated and unrelenting exclusion of happiness and comfort.

His persuasions, while not as well expressed today, are still surefire vote-getters.

Unlike those Quakers in Philadelphia who endorsed an absolute solitary system, no talking, no human communion, Fry thought there should be single cells, but humans working together during the day and windows in cells to see the sky. The cells at Auburn and many other early prisons were "inside cells," with walkways on both the outside walls, so natural light came

50

in only from the windows in the hall. (One hundred windowless cubicles have recently been built at Bedford.) Fry spoke against chains and whipping as well, which were then commonly used against both men and women. She spent her later years bringing her message to the European continent, and it reached the United States and Canada, too. Elizabeth Fry associations in Canada still play an active role in studying and promoting prison reform. One of the prison buildings in Bedford Hills is named in her honor.

By the end of the Civil War, a woman who was to play an important role in the founding of a women's reformatory in Bedford Hills was already sixty-five years old. Her name was Abby Hopper Gibbons, and like Fry she was born into a deeply religious Quaker family. Her mother was a Quaker minister, her father a staunch abolitionist. Like many women reformers of the time, she was also well educated "for a woman." Her father helped to found the Prison Association of New York. Its members visited prisoners in jail and provided help and encouragement to them after they were discharged. Today it is named the Correctional Association of New York and still serves as the guide and conscience and informant of New York's prison system. It is the only public interest organization in New York with legislative authority to visit prisons and report its findings and recommendations to the state legislature. Since Abby's father founded it, it has, over its 144 years of existence, studied every facet of the State prisons, and was instrumental in the State's establishing special facilities for juvenile offenders, and in establishing the first probation and parole services in the State.

Abby became head of the women's division of the Association which was called the WPA, Women's Prison Association. She also raised a large family and experienced the fairly common sadness in those days of losing two children. She served as a nurse during the

51

Civil War, and when the war ended, resumed the struggle to establish separate prisons for women.

A woman named Margaret Fuller, an editor of the New York *Tribune* and obviously well ahead of her time, was one of the first members of the press to publicly defend "the fallen woman." Along with Abby Gibbons and others, she played a role in establishing a halfway house for New York women coming out of prison. A woman "who neither smoked, nor drank, nor cursed," they announced, could find shelter and "learn the Christian virtues and skills that would help them live a better life." Sewing, cooking and other domestic activities were taught, and when she left, a woman was prepared to work as a domestic. The home was named in honor of Abby's father, the Isaac Hopper Home, and is still functioning today. Margaret Fuller wrote a series of articles for the *Tribune* in 1845 asking the public to support the home with money and furniture and to open their hearts to the idea that women could be reformed and welcomed back again into "decent society." By 1854, almost 3,000 women had passed through the home. Of them 480 were considered without hope of being redeemed. The others, a strong number statistically, apparently "made it."

While no one could fault the sincerity and dogged determination of early feminists to help their hapless sisters, the message they preached was quite different from what many feminists teach today. The cause they pled was not the similarities of the sexes. It was their differences. Women, they preached, are unique sexually and superior morally and should be treated differently than men. What brought them down was a combination of "evil associations, hereditary tendencies, poverty, drink, and a lack of kindly aid after the first offense." The last mentioned "lack of kindly aid after the first offense," still rings true and very loud, even today. Government statistics tell us that almost 70 percent of women convicted in this country for a felony had their first arrest for prostitution. Who helped them then? Who helps them now?

In recent prison reports that I have read, written by women, one can still hear some of this same attitude. "Women are different." "Women must be treated equally—but not the same as men." Some feminists, on the other hand, are suggesting coeducational prisons. The move of men into women's prisons as guards came about largely because women demanded an equal right with men to work in the men's prisons.

The prime requirement for female lawbreakers, according to the early feminists, was single-sex institutions managed by women. Society, they said, owed young women a fair chance to be redeemed. Even a few men reformers were beginning to press for single-sex institutions—some, more for their own peace of mind than to serve the women. There were male guards and administrators who swore they would rather be in charge of one hundred male prisoners than five women. I've heard C.O.s at Bedford say the same thing—with deep feeling! The little hothouse flower described as submissive and obedient could also scratch, claw, pull hair, talk in obscenities and in general "go off" as we say in here.

Susan B. Anthony, a radical feminist and a familiar name, served briefly as the superintendent of a women's reformatory and added her strong voice to the growing concern about "wayward girls." In ringing rhetoric she asked, "Weary and worn from her day's toil she sees at every side and at every turn the gilded hand of vice and crime outstretched. Can we wonder that so many poor girls fall?" The "outstretched and gilded hand of vice and crime" became a popular subject for cartoons.

It isn't quite the way the ladies of *MS* magazine would put it today, but among the women I have come to know in this prison, without the flowery prose it's still a relevant question, and a very large problem. Sex and drugs pay well. Slinging hash and selling ribbons do not.

The first women's reformatory in the United States that wasn't attached to a male prison opened surprisingly enough, not in Philadelphia or Boston or New York as one might have expected, but in Indianapolis, Indiana, in 1874, in part through the labors of a Quaker husband and wife named Rhoda and Charles Coffin. It did not follow the tier upon tier architecture of men's prisons and used instead a campus approach with more opportunity to be outdoors than men's prisons offered. The second reformatory opened in Framingham, Massachusetts, in 1887. The next three opened in New York State: the New York House of Refuge in Hudson, New York, in 1887; the Western House of Refuge in Albion, New York, in 1893; and the New York Reformatory for Women, now known as Bedford Hills Correctional Facility, in 1901.

The House of Refuge in Hudson was soon turned into an institution for juveniles twelve to fifteen years of age. The Western House of Refuge at Albion has been used in many ways including as a refuge for female mental defectives, later a coeducational prison, and today it is one of two State medium security prisons for women. What was opened as a reformatory at Bedford is now, many years later, the State's only top security prison for women and called Bedford Hills Correctional Facility.

It is quick work to list their names and dates. It was slow, tedious work to translate them into bricks and mortar. More than any one person, Abby Gibbons is credited with convincing the legislators in Albany that a women's reformatory near New York City was sorely needed. She lobbied personally among members of the State Assembly and in 1889 a bill was passed allowing for a small appropriation to begin the project. The governor vetoed it. Worrying about women prisoners was not a big vote-getter in 1889. It still isn't in 1988.

Gibbons's last trip to Albany to again lobby the cause was made in 1891. She was ninety years old by then and whether it was what she said or the sight of a spunky lady of ninety traveling a long distance to plead her cause, in the following year, 1892, a new law was passed appropriating money to look for a location for a third women's reformatory. The new governor, Governor Flower, signed the bill into law.

The law provided for the appointment by the governor, within thirty days of its signing, of five residents of the state, at least two of whom must be women, to constitute a Board of Managers of the reformatory. It authorized the purchase of a site by the board, in Westchester or New York County, preferably with a suitable building already on it. If such a building couldn't be found, the managers were empowered to contract for its construction. When completed, the board was to appoint a female superintendent as well as other female employees and determine their salaries. Board members were to receive no pay and, in addition, were each required to post a $5,000 bond as proof of their honorable intentions.

The first five managers appointed by the governor were listed in the local paper as:

David Carvalo of New York City

Alice Sanford of Pelham, daughter of the late General Lyman Sanford

John Berry of Mt. Vernon

Arris Huntington of Syracuse, daughter of Bishop Huntington

Samuel Johnson of Rye

Note that only the ladies had to be certified by saying who their fathers were. What stock the men came from wasn't important as long as they were men. Later, a sixth board member was added who had to be a physician.

Abby Gibbons was the first to be asked to serve on the board as its head. She wisely declined and died a year later. Before her death, she wrote to the Board of Managers, "A reformatory pure and simple is my aim. The word 'prison' pray keep in the background. Criminals are made what they are by association and treatment. Let us turn over a new leaf and remember they are human."

Four

Every night and every morn,
Some to misery are born.
Every morn and every night
Some are born to sweet delight.

WILLIAM BLAKE

The Board of Managers decided early on to locate the reformatory in Westchester County. In 1893, it purchased 107½ acres of land at Bedford Station on the Harlem Railroad line for $10,000. A local Westchester paper reported:

One of our citizens, Mr. James Cromwell, has sold his farm of about 110 acres east of this place to the State. The price paid was $10,000. It is understood that the State proposes to build a woman's reformatory there, and expend a large amount of money in necessary buildings and improving the grounds. This property has been selected by a commission of 3, who, from all available property offered, deemed this best suited to their needs, as it has the requisite supply of water, and was just the site for the plans already prepared. This certainly speaks well of

Bedford and Mr. Cromwell's farm in particular.

Whether we were more Christian then or less pragmatic than we are today, I don't know. Our present attitudes toward correctional facilities are aptly reflected in the fact that a new jail for New York City is presently being built on the Canadian border, a nine hour drive from New York City. And somebody thinks it makes sense. "Put 'em in prison. But not in my neighborhood."

Plans for the reformatory buildings to be erected were submitted and approved in December 1893. They included a main building with housing for the superintendent and subordinate officers, a meeting room for the board, a chapel, gymnasium and schoolrooms, four separate cottages to house thirty inmates per cottage, and a three-story dormitory for reception and orientation for 144 women until they could be assigned to a cottage. The facility's total capacity was 264 inmates.

An article in the *Westchester Journal* dated April 27, 1894, announced optimistically, "This week ground will be broken for the buildings, and after many years of work, the Women's Prison Association will know that the much needed institution for which they have labored so hard will soon be an accomplished fact."

Four and one half years later the project was still not complete. According to an article in the *Manual and Civil List of Westchester County* published in 1898, "The program of building the new Reformatory has been greatly retarded by Legislatures ignoring appeals and neglecting to appropriate amounts actually necessary to carry on the work."

After being under construction for almost ten years, in May 1901 the New York Reformatory for Women was finally open for business. Unlike the Madeira School, it doesn't have a Founder's Day celebration every year with large bowls of strawberries and ice cream. I'm told there are even those in the community who would like to forget that anyone did found it.

The opening of the reformatory was celebrated with an informal reception for all interested residents of Bedford Hills. According to the *Mt. Kisco Recorder*, it was a sunny day and "between 200 and 300 people came." That's about as precise as most prison statistics still are. The party lasted from 3:30 P.M. to 6:00 P.M., guests were introduced to matrons and staff and given a tour of the buildings. Later there was tea and cake. "The officers," said the *Recorder*, "all of whom are women, have never held similar positions, although they have spent much time studying work of the sort; they come fresh to their labors having had no opportunity to fall into ruts or bring harsh methods from other institutions." There were three male guards for the outside of the property, and two men in the powerhouse. Everyone else on the staff was a woman. The article added with pardonable pride, "each of the girls' rooms has electricity."

Hostess for the opening day reception was the new superintendent, an interesting woman named Katherine Bement Davis. Discovered and recommended by Josephine Shaw Lowell, member of the State Board of Charities, Davis was enthusiastically endorsed by the entire Board of Managers. "I told them I would take the job if I could run it as a school and not a prison," she said. History has it they told her she could.

Katherine Davis was born in 1860 in Buffalo, New York. Like many of the other bright women of her day, her parents were reformers, too. "I was born a suffragist," she often said. After graduating from high school, she taught school for ten years, and then went to Vassar. After graduating from Vassar, she won a fellowship in political economy at the recently opened University of Chicago. There she studied under Thorstein Veblen and earned her doctorate. By 1901, she was at Bedford, and there she was to stay for thirteen years as superintendent. In the years that followed, she would also earn honorary degrees from Western Reserve University, Mt. Holyoke and Yale, and be made a trustee of Vassar.

It is difficult for many of us today to understand not the intelligence but the courage it took in 1901 to be the woman Katherine Davis was. By the late nineteenth century when women's colleges were springing up, an equally active group of male "experts" were warning parents of long lists of horrendous illnesses that could result in a woman with too much education. Mental exercise in excess could cause the uterus to atrophy, they announced with certitude, and what was woman after all, but a creature built around a uterus. At best, they warned, too much energy spent by a woman on books could shorten her life, leave her barren or cause her to have sickly babies, since the nutrients for her unborn child would have been wasted on her brain.

In her 1981 book, *Their Sisters' Keepers*, Estelle B. Freedman cites a book by Dr. Edward Clark entitled *Sex in Education; or, A Fair Chance for the Girls*, in which he quoted a study made in 1902 of patients entering an insane asylum. Forty-two percent of the women entering were "well educated." Sixteen percent of the men were "well educated," significant statistical proof he said, that "too much education drives women crazy."

The lives of three special women, Elizabeth Fry, Abby Gibbons and Katherine Davis span over one hundred and fifty years, and each played a role, however peripheral or basic, in the institution where I am now committed and therefore in my life as well. At the risk of sounding girlish, I find that exciting, a little the way I felt one day in Warsaw when an old gentleman told me of an afternoon in Leningrad when he and his wife were raking leaves and heard all the commotion and ran to the Neva River to discover "Those crazy

60

Bolsheviks had taken the Winter Palace." Feeling close to history makes me feel alive, as though life were more sane than it seems at first glance to be, even as though the world might have a plan or a purpose.

Women sentenced to the reformatory at Bedford were to be between the ages of sixteen and thirty and were to be sentenced to not less than three nor more than five years, unless they were discharged earlier by the Board of Managers, which in addition to its other duties also acted as parole board. After nine months here, a woman could be considered for parole, or she might serve the full three or five years for simple misdemeanors. This was considerably longer than a man would serve for the same crime. But then, men didn't have to be reformed like women, and reforming takes time. Many years later, in 1974, the reformatory sentence would be declared unconstitutional.

Crimes for which a girl or woman could be sent here included petty larceny, habitual drunkenness, being a "common and disorderly person, violating the tenement house law, endangering the morals of children, frequenting chop suey houses of bad repute, or any other misdemeanor or felony except murder, manslaughter, burglary, or arson." I have not learned authoritatively what it took to damage a chop suey house's repute. Perhaps those were the places where the Chinese sold back to us some of the opium we sold to them. There are fine old family fortunes in this country that were built upon opium sales. The granddaughters of some of the drug kingpins of today will come out under striped tents at Newport some day. And meanwhile the small-time lackeys who deliver the stuff, or pick up the scraps from the table, will go to jail.

Women found guilty of murder, manslaughter, burglary or arson went to prison, not a reformatory, and those insane or "mentally or physically incapable of benefitting from reformatory discipline" were also to

61

be excluded.

In practice, not only female offenders who had committed the more serious crimes, but females who looked "more masculine," or in fact were members of minorities, continued to be sent to custodial institutions like Auburn prison, under the supervision of men. After the New York Reformatory opened, an increasing proportion of the Auburn female population was black. By 1913, half of it was black, while 5 percent of Bedford was black.

A large proportion of Auburn was also foreign-born, especially Irish and German. Judges, influenced as we all are by stereotypes, and left with many arbitrary calls to make, saved for the reformatories those who looked more conventional, less threatening, more capable of being resocialized and able to meet middle-class standards of womanliness. This they believed excluded most blacks. The few blacks who did come to Bedford while Davis was here lived desegregated among the other women. She would not hear of segregation.

The story is told of a young white prisoner who was listed as "hopeful" for reformation until it was learned that her mother and father had never married. She slipped down to "less hopeful." Strict moral intolerance was alive and well when reformatories were at their most influential. Some of the roots of that early intolerance have some healthy sprouts still alive today. Many people in America look down on inmates for having done some of the things quite common in their own families, and millions of other families as well. The cruel hypocrisy of our drug laws is a grim example.

One year and a half after its opening, word had it that the reformatory was about to be closed. In a letter to the editor February 21, 1903, in the *Westchester Journal,* a distressed lady wrote high praise for the work of superintendent Davis,

Other methods sometimes thought useful in such institutions she has laid aside as tending to debase and degrade rather than to uplift. For a year and three quarters this policy has prevailed and it can fairly be said by those competent to judge, this effort has produced encouraging results. And now to the astonishment of the friends of the institution who . . . have now begun to rejoice in the promise of success, the reformatory is to be wiped out of existence by the State officials at Albany, who are out of sympathy with its spirit or unaware of its usefulness.

Perhaps it is not surprising that men in the strife and stress of public life, busy with its cares and contests and victories, should fail to appreciate the feelings and purposes of men and women who believe in matters like these. But it is somewhat strange, though not by any means new, that men whom we are accustomed to call practical politicians should fail to take into account the existence of these worthy though perhaps visionary people whose numbers are great, and whose memories are good.

Which qualifies for the ladylike-threat-of-the-year award. Whether anyone of note read the letter I can't say, but I find no more discussion about closing the facility.

For the most part, the education that Davis introduced at Bedford was "gender specific" and based on the premise that inmates were fairly childlike and domestic. Even the early punishments started out as the old familiar ones my mother at one time or another inflicted upon me as a child; sent to one's room; sent to bed without dinner; missing a treat; and having your mouth washed out with soap. Years later, when customs had changed drastically, testifying at a hearing as to whether women at Bedford had been cruelly treated, Davis admitted that she had personally washed some mouths out with soap when girls used "unseemly language." If such a punishment were to be resurrected here today, I would urge my sons to buy stock in soap companies.

Nicole Rafter, in her book, *Prisons for Women,* stated that reformatories, for all their good intentions, institutionalized the double standard. Davis might or might not have argued the point. Independent, well-educated professional woman that she was, it is questionable that she could realistically consider herself a role model for most of her charges. For them, their preparation for life was that of a domestic, who if hired by a particularly generous family, could expect to earn $2.50 a week.

Yet Davis, for all the emphasis on hearth and nursery, was innovative for her day. She emphasized the importance of the "cottage system" with plenty of outdoor activities and recreation. The inhumane tiers of metal cages, she believed, should be done away with, for men as well as for women. Parole, she believed and practiced, should be granted as early as possible. "No person should be kept in prison," she said, "if she can be cared for outside with safety for society and for herself." Her Board of Managers agreed.

The superintendent of the reformatory at Framingham, Massachusetts explained to an early audience, "We never parole a girl until she can bake bread." Her audience clapped approvingly. Davis said, "We don't parole a girl until she has a marketable skill, whether it is a nontraditional female skill or not." We're still talking about those "nontraditional" skills for women in 1988, but the skills being taught here at Bedford today are fewer than they were in 1905, and they're hardly nontraditional.

Every inmate who came to Bedford while Davis was

here was required to take academic classes, to do manual labor and to do a good many domestic tasks as well. A girl was offered lessons in basic reading and writing and arithmetic, through algebra if she could cope, current events, mechanical drawing, gymnastics, singing lessons, physiology and sex hygiene. College students were encouraged to volunteer over the summer to tutor and to give plays with the women. In addition to all facets of domestic science, a girl could learn tailoring, chair caning, shoe repair, bookbinding, painting, carpentry, hat making, machine knitting, stenography, typing and hospital aide skills. All types of outdoor work were encouraged, and some required. Each girl had a garden and played some role in raising chickens, slaughtering pigs and breeding stock. They also did masonry work, built roads, shoveled coal, harvested ice in the winter and drained swamps.

The early twentieth century, just growing accustomed to America's move from farm to city, had many active students of sociology and crime who pictured city dwellers as victims of insufficient light and air and exercise. The unhealthy city life, they preached (with foresight), could lead to all manner of dismal results, including crime. Davis herself, a firm believer in the importance of work and exercise in the great outdoors, wrote an article entitled, "The Fresh Air Treatment for Moral Disease." We never stop seeking a painless cure for our own behavior. We didn't then. We don't today.

How the young ladies felt about the curriculum I don't know. Some who spoke for them made it sound like a jolly place indeed. There was someone named Barrows, writing in 1910, who described the young ladies this way: "With wheelbarrows and spade the girls joyfully smoothed down the hills and terraced the slopes, the state paying only for the grass seed."

Babies born to the incarcerated women were delivered in a community hospital, and then brought back to the reformatory nursery, to be raised there, in rare cases for as long as two years, by which time most young mothers had been paroled. After a month's recovery, the young mothers went back to work, and many inmates took turns in the nursery caring for the babies. Mothers could then be with the children in the late afternoon and evening, much as a working mother would.

Another important part of Davis's philosophy for administering a reformatory involved classifying the inmates by age, background and behavior. She considered it a basic first step in helping people to learn as much about them as one could, their mental capacities, their physical conditions, their family backgrounds, their cultural habits. Women were assigned to one of the four cottages according to what was learned. As more cottages were added, classification could be more precise. Each cottage had its own gardens, linens, china and separate rooms for each girl.

There were many nineteenth-century reformers who believed that separate prisons for women and a heady dose of domestication would solve most of the criminality among them. Studies made at Bedford and other places as well made it clear that the problems of many were far too complicated to be solved by cradle rocking and a good loaf of bread. Many of the women, then as now, had to support themselves. Strange how many of us speak of that as though it were something new. And as long as crime paid better than honest labor, many would opt for crime. They still do — for the same reason.

On the women's page of the *Denver Post,* July 1905, was an article about Sylvia Pankhurst, member of a militant suffragette family in England. She was visiting this country to study our prisons for women. She was duly impressed with what she saw at Bedford and announced that England had nothing like it, and would have a hard time trying to establish something comparable. "In England a girl over 16 must go to prison whatever her crime. We have no reformatory for her. Of Bedford she said, 'The finest I have ever seen. . . . Excellent and wholesome. The food was good . . . and as for the sleeping quarters and other accommodations, I cannot speak too highly of them. Each girl has a room to herself and is even allowed her own little trifles.' "

Five

I love you, said the great mother.
I love you for what you are/
knowing so much what you are.
CARL SANDBURG, "WINDSONG"

The young women arriving here today in big Department of Corrections buses from Rikers Island
could in many ways be contemporaries of the women
Katherine Davis wrote about in 1912 in a work entitled, *A Study of Prostitutes Committed From New York City
to the State Reformatory for Women at Bedford Hills*.

There is a far larger proportion of black women here
now than then, and the "foreign-born" are from Puerto
Rico instead of Eastern Europe. More than ever in its
history, Bedford stands today as a monument to America's racism. The economic, social and demographic
changes in those seventy-six years are immense, but
the women themselves, their life stories, their culture
of poverty, remain essentially the same. They were —
like many of my near neighbors today — young, poor,
uneducated, unhealthy, prostitutes somewhere in their
working careers; highly emotional and excitable; egocentric in the extreme; obscene; and the children of

68

broken families as the result of death, illness, desertion, imprisonment, alcohol or drug addiction. Unlike today, 67 percent were white Americans, 28 percent foreign born and 5 percent black. Today, 20 percent are white, 52 percent are black, and 28 percent are Puerto Rican. A recent study commissioned by the state predicts that 90 percent of New York State prisoners will be minority members by the year 2000.

I often found a sad irony, while the song was so popular, in those ringing first words, "We are the world." It is the song of newborn infants, too. At birth, the only world we know is what we can see and touch ourselves. When the infant can't see a mother's face, she has ceased to exist. The thinking of many of the women here has progressed only a few halting steps further along the road to adulthood than this. Ignorance, and the lack of caring adults who had time for them, has hooded their eyes. They cannot see the larger picture. But then, that isn't characteristic only of inmates, so perhaps it's out of order to mention here.

It was the American-born girls of foreign-born parents that contributed the largest percentage of inmates in 1912, far over their percentage of the total population. Mother and father knew little English and only old world customs. At an early age their children believed they knew more than their parents did, and then, as now, that made for a bad beginning.

Generalizing about her years of observing hundreds of troubled young women, Davis wrote, "An observation extending over twelve years of the relations between foreign-born fathers and mothers and their American-born daughters, leads me to believe that right here lies one of the important points of attack in preventive work. . . . The most important factor in the study of any individual is the kind of family from which she comes."

Writing sixty-five years later, James Q. Wilson of

Harvard observed, "The true causes of delinquency can be found in the absence of parental affection, coupled with family conflict, inconsistent discipline, and rebellious parents."

It is clear from her writings that Davis knew a great deal more about her charges than is known about the incarcerated woman today. "Treat the criminal, not the crime," she often said, and to do so meant first finding out about the criminal. An organized study was made of each young woman who arrived at the reformatory, with statistics collected on her family background, health, education, marital status, children and work record. Field trips were made to interview parents.

Davis's information was gathered from personal interviews and information from correspondence with previous employers, letters sent and received by the women themselves (they were read going out and coming in then; today only incoming mail is opened), from the officers who chaperoned all visits to the girls while in the institutions, and "from," as she put it, "personal acquaintance extending in every case from three months to several years."

The role of head of a girls' school, as well as the superintendent of a reformatory, was far more intrusive seventy-five years ago than it is today. I have read old report cards written by Mabel Thomas and Lucy Madeira as well, lecturing Mother and Father on the child's need for regular doses of castor oil and mother's need to make the elastic in Susie's bloomers looser, ending with a brief lecture on who her friends should be. That such intrusions into one's private life are no longer acceptable is a kind of progress itself and yet there are many families out there who could use a lecture from Mabel Thomas or Lucy Madeira or Katherine B. Davis, even today, especially today.

Davis believed, as one could well do today, that "the women convicted in the courts are not a fair sample of New York prostitutes as a class, for the reasons that the more prosperous ones are so protected as not to suffer molestation from the police." She had a splendid, ladylike way of saying what was then and is still today, disgusting, but true.

There were no women at the reformatory who had committed murder, manslaughter or arson in 1912. Those women were sent to Auburn Prison for Women until 1930. Even at Auburn, the percentage of women found guilty of violent crimes was less than it is today. Grand larceny was the crime of choice then, 42 percent as against 6 percent today. Three percent of the women at Auburn were there for murder and 9 percent for manslaughter. Today at Bedford, 9 percent are here for murder and 19 percent for manslaughter. Since many of the cases today are the result of domestic violence, one might conclude they are the result of women's new attitude toward themselves, their willingness to stand just so much battering by a man, and then no more.

The largest number of foreign-born women incarcerated in New York State in 1912 were Russian, reflecting the flight from pogroms. Next came Austro-Hungarian, German, Irish, English, Scots, French and Italian, in that order. Today, the fastest growing group, and largest non-English-speaking group, is Puerto Rican. The number of European- and Asian-born women here is negligible, one from Taiwan, three from Hong Kong, one from the Philippines, one Russian, one Yugoslavian, one Pole, several Germans and Italians, little more.

There is a good deal of difference between the attitudes of foreign-born women in 1912, and the attitudes one sees here in the Puerto Rican women. In 1912, people came here with the idea of becoming American citizens, learning English, raising their children as Americans, living out the rest of their lives here. The number of foreign-born women who ended up incarcerated in the first part of the century was a smaller portion than their percentage of the city's total population in every case. For example, in 1912 those who were Russian born made up 10 percent of the city's total population, but only 8 percent of those imprisoned.

Today, Puerto Ricans are automatically granted American citizenship, and Puerto Rico is close enough by for them to fly back and forth to "the old country" frequently. They cling to their own language and own customs to the point where many may live here for five or ten or fifteen years and still have not learned English. They come here to make money, more than to make a new home, and they raise their children, many of them, to speak Spanish, not English. They are coming into this prison today faster than any other group, and well above their percentage of the total city population.

For a while, reflecting the flight of so many Jews from Eastern Europe, a large proportion of Jewish immigrants began to arrive in Bedford and Auburn. The proportion of Jewish women in the total reformatory population rose from 11.3 percent in 1911 to 18.8 percent in 1912. Obviously, antisemitism abroad is what brought them here. Whether it played a role in their being imprisoned in this country I don't know. For the next ten years, special religious and social services were established for Jewish inmates, and in 1920 Alice Davis Menkin was the first Jew to become a member of the Board of Managers. Today at Bedford, the number of Jewish inmates is far below the proportion of Jews in the total New York population, but some of the most loyal and hardworking volunteers are Jewish. There are also few Asian women here. They seem to be going to college instead of to prison, and many have their own system of justice in the areas where they live. Numbers and faces in here tell a great deal about the advantages and disadvantages of various cultures. They can be a source of great strength or an albatross — and since it is now looked down upon as very unkind, if not unconstitutional, to try to change the cultural habits of others, some of the albatrosses are hanging heavier and heavier.

The educational level of the reformatory inmates was lower than it is here today, but the whole country's level was lower. In spite of it, more of the reformatory women were employed when they were arrested than those today, 95 percent as against 65 percent. Those figures reflect the absence of welfare checks in 1912, and a larger supply of jobs available for the uneducated.

Mothers and fathers of Davis's charges, if both were living, often both worked, and the eight-hour day was a thing of the distant future. Their work days could be ten to twelve hours long. Of the 647 women Davis included in her study, the fathers of 245 were deceased, and 195 mothers were deceased. Tuberculosis took many of them. Women are again entering this prison with tuberculosis, although with proper medical care it should not happen.

The most dramatic difference between the two groups is in marriage. In 1912 52 percent of the women were married, 23 percent widowed, and 6 percent divorced. None claimed a common-law husband. Today approximately 12 percent of the women are married, 3 percent widowed, 8 percent divorced and 15 percent claim a common-law husband. In short 81 percent of the women in 1912 were or had been married. Today 23 percent are or have been married.

It was a rare unmarried woman in 1912 who would admit to having a baby. Though there was a nursery here from the reformatory's beginning, I find no mention of it by Davis, or even a mention of the number of children an inmate had. The emphasis was all on reformation, and little babies didn't need any — or so we then thought.

Family life of the two groups of women was tragically similar in ways other than marriage, the same violence and ugliness that poverty creates. Both groups came from larger than average families, and size of family played a role then, as it may today in a girl's turning to prostitution. As Davis explained it, the oldest daughter often served as housemaid, nurse and drudge through most of her childhood and finally kicked over the traces and ran away to "lead a life of her own."

Large families are not unusual with the women who live here today. I have three close neighbors whose families consist of fifteen, eighteen and nineteen siblings respectively. Mothers and daughters in here frequently have children the same age.

The role of men in family life has changed tragically in the past twenty-five years, for many reasons, but with one grim result: too many children born to those having no intention of playing the role of parent or provider. I read recently of a thirty-year-old man living in several rooms with two women and eleven of his nineteen children in the Hotel Bryant, a welfare hotel. With great pride, he showed the interviewer a picture of his thirteen-year-old crack-dealing son. "He's the only one of my kids to graduate from sixth grade," the man said. He is the sheik of midtown Manhattan, one of many with a larger harem than the Aga Khan's.

Willie Mae told me, "Shit. Ma brother got him I guess fifty kids. When one a them new cousins come in ma house now I don't even wanna hear his name." Gwen told me, "We got a boy on my block, eighteen-year old, had him five babies last year. An' I know, cause one a them babies was mine."

One of the characteristics of Davis's reformatory girls which has lasted unchanged over the years is their cavalier attitude toward money. There are women here who have over the years earned three times what I earned in a lifetime of teaching, but they have never owned a house or had any kind of permanence in their

74

lives. The reason: They spend money as fast as they earn it.

Davis wrote of the women, "It is our general experience that the majority of prostitutes have little conception of the value of money. They earn it easily and spend it easily. Even among those who claim to make far more than the wages of well-paid working girls, it is not infrequent to find young women without changes of underwear."

I have watched women on commissary day, many times, struggle mightily with the amount of money in their commissary fund to be absolutely sure that every penny is spent. If she has $11.87, she will add and subtract all the evening before she shops figuring how she can come out even. With $60 she does the same, and that's the limit she can spend in the commissary in a two-week period.

The health of the women of 1912 was precarious, as it is today. Their mothers had had little or no prenatal care and many of them as children had had unhealthy diets and unhealthy habits of personal hygiene. Today, the life expectancy of black women is eight years less than that of white women, and black infant deaths are twice as prevalent as those of white infants. Of the more than six hundred women included in a study Davis did of prostitutes, just under 90 percent tested positive for gonorrhea and/or syphilis when they arrived at Bedford. What percentage arriving today has herpes, gonorrhea or test positive for the AIDS virus, I don't know. I do know fifteen women from here have died of AIDS in the past year and a half. A few even test positive for syphilis, but the cure today is far gentler than it was in 1912. Many of the women had to be virtually forced to take the cure then. Today, it is no longer legal to force any of the women to take any medication, but most take what's given them.

The reasons women give for entering prostitution today are essentially the same collection of reasons they gave Davis. Whether they are honest answers is anyone's guess. More women today list "I needed the money" or "I liked the money" as their reasons. More women then said, "I yielded to the man I loved." Other reasons are miscellaneous: "I was forced," "I can't remember," "I happen to like it." More women in 1912 admitted turning all or part of their earnings over to their lovers. Today, that lover is known as a pimp and is still very much part of her life.

Drinking and drugs played a heavy role then as now in the incarcerated woman's life, but addiction was not the pervasive problem that it is today. It wasn't until the middle and upper classes began to partake, especially of drugs, that society became concerned and large numbers of both men and women began coming to prison for use, possession and sale of same. Today, in spite of horrendous prison terms for possession and selling of drugs, they are sold more openly and in greater quantities than ever before, in all levels of society. As of January 1988, the number of inmates serving time for drug-related offenses surpassed those imprisoned for any other crime. There are forty-one thousand prisoners in fifty state prisons in New York State, and 20 percent of them are here for selling or possessing drugs. The number of prisoners in the state prisons has increased by just under 50 percent in the past five years. The number of drug convictions among them has increased by 300 percent, and many of the robbery and burglary offenses, while not listed as drug charges, were motivated by drugs.

I saw no indication in my reading that the reformatory had a drug treatment program or anything like AA, which would be invented many years later. The addiction program was simply "Thou shalt not." Today at Bedford we have an AA program, NA (Narcotics Anonymous) and even a program for those obsessed with money, called the Money Addiction program. The trouble is the programs aren't large enough or numerous enough to treat all those who need help.

According to the Correctional Association of New York, twenty-five thousand people incarcerated in New York State prisons today have drug or alcohol problems, and many of their crimes are attributable to this. Notwithstanding, only two thousand prisoners can be accommodated in the existing substance-abuse programs at one time. Most of these programs become available to a prisoner at the end of her sentence, not the beginning, so a woman may come here addicted, spend five years or more using any kind of drugs she can beg, borrow or steal, and then, six months before going back on the street, enter a drug-abuse program. She needs it from the start to the finish of her time here, and even then she may go back to drugs on the street. I've seen drugs pull mothers away from children I know they love. It is an evil master, and those driven by it need far more treatment in prison than they currently get.

When a reformatory woman or girl was ready to go out to work but not quite eligible for parole, she was often "indentured" to a local family as a domestic servant. If she quit the job before a given time, she was returned to the reformatory. Today, there is no "indentured program" before a woman may be eligible for parole. There is instead "work-release" and she is eligible for it two years before parole. Unfortunately, while many may be eligible only a few are called because there is only one place in New York City a woman may live while on work-release: Parkside, at West 121st Street and Mt. Morris Park West. I'm told by women who have lived there that there's a "base-house" next door, the newsstand on the corner is a front for dealing coke and the park across the street is such a popular gathering place for drug buyers and sellers that Parkside women are forbidden to walk through it. If de Sade had picked the spot it couldn't be a worse place to help troubled addicts start life anew.

For a few years in the early 1970s, women at Bedford were permitted to leave this facility, work all day and then return here in the evening. Some of us invited members of the community to a meeting three years ago, to see how they would respond to the idea of this being started again. Their response was positive. The administration's was not, and, though I have neither seen nor heard any opinion from Albany, I am told it's out of the question. My only reservation would be not that there aren't a substantial number of women who could and would go out and be useful, but that those making the choices would not pick the logical women to go. Flattery and flirting often go a lot further in here than a good day's work.

Six

*We remove cruelty from the neighborhood and make
it the sickness of perverse strangers.*

SHERRY TURKLE

What makes some of us "good" and some of us "evil"
is an age-old question. Who *is* good and who *is* evil is
just as puzzling. It is easy to report about people and
places, and hard to reflect about them, especially on
paper where others can judge you for being judgmental.

I often read the essays of Simone Weil. She is a hard
taskmaster. I stumble and worry about how clumsy I
am when I reread her admonition, "Writers do not
have to be professors of morals, but they do have to
express the human condition." Up to that point I feel
reasonably safe, but then she adds, "And nothing concerns human life so essentially for every man at every
minute as good and evil. When literature becomes deliberately indifferent to the opposition of good and
evil, it betrays its function and forfeits all claims to
excellence." Heaven knows I am not indifferent to the
subject. I once believed the questions of good and evil
were childishly simple to solve, like telling the differ-

ence between black and white. Then I grew up and discovered a world with hundreds of shades of gray. And then I came to prison and discovered so much evil in the box labeled "Good," and some genuine good in the box marked "Evil," that I would never again presume it was child's play to distinguish between the two.

Deciding who is good and who is evil is a chancey business. History teaches us that. Drawing the line between crime and sin is tricky, too. Black's *Law Dictionary* defines crime, but not sin. Historically man's early concept of crime equated it with "demonology." Criminals were "possessed." There was little or no distinction between crime and sin since established rules were considered God-given. In the sixteenth century, a workhouse called the Bridewell was built in London, and it housed the sick and old and destitute, as well as petty thieves and pickpockets, reflecting the common notion that "poverty was basically the result of immorality and not so much different from thieving." That so many of our incarcerated today are poor is an indication that four hundred years later we still cling to that notion, whether we like to be told so or not.

Until the 1820s in England, it was legal to whip a person for having smallpox. In a decision in 1862, the United States Supreme Court wrote, "To know the right and still the wrong pursue proceeds from a perverse will brought about by the seduction of the Evil one." Today we imprison people, at huge expense to the public, because they cannot get through the month on their welfare checks and cheat us out of hundreds of dollars whenever they can or whenever they must. For the satisfaction of delivering this punishment we pay a minimum of $25,000 a year, and the punishment may be for two years or more.

Lila served two years for lying about a $167 welfare check. She was offered one year if she would plea bargain, but she refused, went to trial and got two years. She still insists she didn't cash that check. "I think it was ma cousin done it, but I didn't get that money." When she had served her sentence, she hadn't learned anything about how to budget her pennies and get through the month with her four children on her welfare check. She can barely read and write and for two years she wasn't required to try. You and I both know someone who took a $200 income tax deduction at least once last week for a business lunch. Is there any more reason for the taxpayer to pay for that lunch than for Lila's welfare check? I simply pose the question.

There are, and have probably been since we began observing one another's behavior and judging it, two main attitudes toward those we label criminal. The classical school, or hard-line approach, believes that people commit crime as an act of free will because, one must suppose, they are evil. The determinist school, sometimes called the bleeding heart approach, believes man is propelled to do what he does by social forces, over which he may or may not have any control.

The classical school believes for whatever reasons someone breaks the rule, he's no damned good and must be harshly punished. In fact, the harsher the better. The determinist thinks we should try to find out why the crime was committed so that at the least we can save the next generation from repeating the same mistake.

We've learned over the years many of the characteristics of those who go to jail, but it is only recently that we have begun to concentrate on the qualities of those who don't go to jail. It is a fairly reliable rule of thumb that an abused child of an alcoholic mother and drug-ridden father, who has lived a loveless existence in poverty, will not grow up to be an admirable, productive, upstanding citizen. But then again, he or she may. In fact enough of these young people survive as useful citizens for doctors to be studying them and searching out what the gifts of personality are that have seen them through what destroys many others. Robert

81

Coles, who has studied and written extensively about children in all socioeconomic levels, writes, as do so many others, "Family is the prime agent for treatment of crime." In those children who "make it" without family support he finds these qualities, "pluck, whimsy, doggedness, a willingness to face down tragedy, stoicism, a gentle soul and a gentleness of manner, compassion for others, religious sensibility, and sensitivity to moral and psychological nuances."

There's a lovely, old-fashioned sound to some of those words. I find it a splendid list, but is it fair to expect the poor to have all that good stuff when so many of the rest of us don't? In a similar study reported in *The New York Times,* October 1987, these qualities were observed in young survivors of the squalor and hopelessness of poverty: a secure attachment to mother and the ability later, if necessary, to seek strength and friendship from other adults, whether a teacher, neighbor or someone else; an independent attitude; high tolerance for frustration; cheerfulness; persistence; a high level of social intelligence and at least average intellectual skills. They are both interesting lists and one can only suppose they come as gifts from God to those lucky ones who then work at them and won't give up. Having listed them, perhaps we may begin to learn how to instill them in those not as lucky or not as gifted. We must, of course, love them a great deal to take the trouble.

Faith in a final "scientific" answer to why people do as they do was deeper and more unquestioning in the years Katherine Davis ran the Bedford reformatory than it is today. The newly invented IQ tests at the beginning of the century were considered by many as absolutely scientific, a breakthrough into the mystery of the mind. Davis was troubled by the low results many of the Bedford women achieved and concluded that the test measured mental training, not mental capacity.

Arguments about the same question go on today. Some say the tests are biased against minorities. I see no way they could not be. A test must be for one culture at a time and entrance into the working and educational life of one culture at a time. Doing poorly on a culturally biased test, whether biased in favor of black society or white society or the culture of Samoa, does not indicate you may not be able in the ways of another culture. But it does indicate you may have some difficult catching up to do if you are to "make it," legally, in that other culture. Everyone is a member of a cultural minority somewhere not far from home. The problem is not so much the tests as the tragic determination of some minority groups to live one culture and enjoy the fruits of another.

Most of us like our questions about why people do as they do to have one easy-to-understand answer. Early solutions to the question of crime could often be satisfactorily answered with a medieval version of Flip Wilson's famous line, "The devil made me do it." With the passage of time, the answers became more complicated, but possibly no less naive.

At the end of the nineteenth century, an Italian biological determinist and student of eugenics named Cesare Lombroso offered the "scientific" explanation, after measuring hundreds of heads and bodies, that crime was a matter of physiology. He could, he boasted, separate prostitutes from good, honest middle-class women, by certain easily discernible physical characteristics. And prostitutes then were all considered synonymous with "the female criminal." There were even serious recommendations made in the 1930s that "selective sterilization" be used as an alternative to committing prostitutes to prison. There were still studies made into the 1970s based on the theory that prostitution is evidence of psychopathology.

Lombroso wrote, "The woman, as distinguished from the man . . . stands at one or other extremity of poles, being either perfectly normal, or excessively anomalous. And when the anomaly is excessive, suicide and madness are one. Consequently, women are very rarely criminal when compared with men, but when criminals, are infinitely worse." Surprisingly enough, this comes close to the theme of John Updike's recent novel, *The Witches of Eastwick,* which some found amusing and whose eighteenth-century theme apparently some still believe. He wrote, "Once a woman has descended from the pedestal of innocence . . . she is prepared to perpetrate every crime."

Lombroso also found a strong relationship between the structure of the skull, bodily characteristics and crime, but only in women, not men. Receding foreheads, he said, are more prevalent among prostitutes, 12 percent as against 8 percent. "Prostitutes are almost quite free of wrinkles, crooked noses, and asymmetrical faces; what they have more frequently are moles, hairiness, prehensile feet, the virile larynx, large jaws and cheekbones, and above all, anomalous teeth." He added that they had little maternal feeling and poor senses of vision, hearing, smell and taste. Sad to say, for many years he was called "the father of scientific criminology."

The connection between crime and physical appearance was hardly an idea new to Lombroso. From virtually the beginning of recorded time, humans have believed, or suspected, that appearance and character were closely related. Homer's heroes were always handsome and splendid. His villains were often grotesque. Socrates's enemies wrote of him, "His face shows him to be a brutal man." Socrates said, "All vice is ignorance. No one is willfully evil," but Aristotle, student of Plato, drew strong parallels between one's morality and physical characteristics. Shakespeare wrote of Cassius, "He has a lean and hungry look . . . such men are dangerous." More recently, in R. L. Stevenson's *The Strange Case of Dr. Jekyll and Mr. Hyde,* to become evil Mr. Hyde was first made to appear evil. *The Portrait of Dorian Gray* is another expression of the same idea, reversed. If you were evil, it would eventually be reflected in your face.

Today, Dr. Stanton Samenow in his book, *Inside the Criminal Mind,* would have us believe that family and environment have nothing to do with crime, no more than facial appearance. "Crime is always voluntary," he writes. "It is criminals who make crime, not families and bad environment," in short, bad seed. His theory doesn't explain why some people choose crime and others don't. There are reasons we make decisions.

Katherine Davis believed that biology played a role in crime, or qualities that can contribute to crime, like quirks of personality, the way two people respond to similar situations, the tendency to be easily habituated to alcohol or drugs, some forms of feeblemindedness, and others, but she was a firm believer that environment played just as active a role. And so am I. How many times have I looked at a girl in here and wondered how different her life would have been if the accident of birth had brought her to a different neighborhood. So many would never have come here.

Though Lombroso's theories about a physiological criminal type were not difficult to disprove, the idea that crime is hereditary remained popular. It has new significance today, with stronger arguments in its behalf than Lombroso could muster. These include studies made both here and abroad of identical twins who have been proven statistically more apt to end up in prison, even if raised by different middle-class families, if their biological father had been in prison. They also include the recent discovery of an extra Y chromosome making a sex determining triplet of chromosomes in some men. Such men, of those known and studied, show a tendency to break the law that is ten to twenty times greater than such a tendency in genetically normal men from comparable populations. The more one reads the studies made about crime and the human mind the more one is left with the inevitable conclusion that there is still much more to be learned; and until then it is safe to say we are the products of our genes and the culture in which we grow up, which combined create what Wilson and Davis were talking about — family.

Seven

*Or have we eaten on the insane root
That takes the reason prisoner.*

MACBETH

The problems of administering a prison or living in one as an inmate appear to me to be quite similar today to the ones that soon came to the fore in the reformatory: mental illness, physical illness, ignorance, drugs and alcohol, racism, overcrowding, inadequate vocational training, incompetent staff and homosexuality. Were I to be asked to choose, I would put mental illness at the top of the list. There are days on my floor when the shrieks and screams and banging on the metal doors and throwing of furniture against a wall make my blood run cold, leave me touching a blanket or a book or something that represents sanity and a degree of permanence in a world gone mad. To tell you the truth, I have a picture of Cider in my cell, the golden retriever I once owned, and sometimes I touch that to give it a friendly pat. It helps.

And while the shrieking goes on, quite often the staff's reaction is to pretend they don't hear it. This is especially their modus operandi while someone is yelling at them in the most obscene possible way, "Motherfuckin' dumb white ass honkie," "Fuckin' Captain, fuckin' bulldagger with gray pants." They sit and gossip in the bubble while chaos rules. Don't ask me what they should do, because I don't know either. The only thing I'm sure of is that locking the mentally ill into cages is not the answer to anything.

Overcrowding was what exacerbated otherwise manageable problems at the reformatory as it has so many places today. In less than four years after it opened, the reformatory was overcrowded. Davis was persuasive enough to have three more cottages added by 1911, and a separate school building completed in 1909. But by the time those were added, still more space was needed. Lesbianism was first mentioned as a problem in the Annual Report of the Board of Managers in 1908 under the rubric of "abnormal attachments." To have to discuss it in mixed company must have been awkward. The last adjective anyone would have attached to it was "gay."

The presence of a growing number of women with mental problems, "mental defectives" as many referred to them, was first mentioned at some length in the Board's Annual Report of 1909. I can only wonder what is said about them in today's Annual Report to the Department of Corrections. By the fall of 1910, the problem, which has never gone away, was serious enough for Davis to apply to the New York Foundation for a grant large enough to provide for a full-time psychologist on the staff. The grant was given and Dr. Jean Weidensall was appointed. She eventually put the findings of her work into a book entitled, *The Mentality of Criminal Women*. She also made strong recommendations to the courts in New York City as to the best placements and treatment for such women. It was through her that John D. Rockefeller, Jr. first heard of the work at Bedford.

That same year, 1910, New York City papers were filled with lurid tales of the "white slave trade." One of the members of a Grand Jury called to investigate the problem was John D. Rockefeller, Jr. He shared Davis's and Weidensall's deep concern for the problems of prostitution and felt that if they were properly investigated and studied they could be, if not eliminated, at least diminished. He decided to build a Laboratory of Social Hygiene to study prostitutes and what it was that sent a woman down to this level of degradation. Davis assured him she knew just the place to build it and showed him ninety acres of available farmland directly across the road from the New York Reformatory.

Mr. Rockefeller bought the land and built a laboratory center, with the main building named in honor of Elizabeth Fry. For the next six years, he financed the entire program with a staff of psychiatrists and psychologists from all over the country, many of them graduates of the Seven Sisters. The state paid a dollar a year rent. With an increased staff, without the attendant financial problems that usually brings, Davis's dream of proper classification of the women sent to Bedford came as close as it ever would to being realized.

Davis had earlier written and made speeches about the first steps she thought should be taken to help solve the problems of prostitution. The first step she believed was to do away with fines for arrested prostitutes. Davis argued, logically, that since the money to pay the fines was inevitably supplied by her pimp, the prostitute usually left jail more indebted to the person who profited by her illegal activity. Unfortunately in spite of the logic of her thinking such fines are still levied on each arrested prostitute — sometimes as many as twenty times a year.

Secondly, she urged the establishment of a city or county "clearinghouse" where each arrestee could be "scientifically studied to determine what had led to a woman's life of crime." "Before we are in a position to deal fairly with a problem," she wrote, "we must know all the elements which enter into it." Having done this, we could then recommend the proper placement of each woman. Obviously, Davis took the word "reformatory" literally. She had no intention of running a punishment warehouse. The establishment by Mr. Rockefeller of the Laboratory of Social Hygiene was, she believed, a giant step forward in social progress. I doubt that many other people even noticed it.

From 1912 to 1918, every woman entering Bedford was first tested and studied in the Laboratory of Social Hygiene. By 1915 enough had been diagnosed as psychopathic to convince Mr. Rockefeller that a special facility for treating them was needed. At his expense, a small hospital was built on the grounds near the laboratory.

According to Dr. Edith Spaulding, who became its head, there was no other facility like it, dedicated to the experimental treatment of psychopathic delinquent women, then in existence. The hospital was in operation from 1916 to 1918. By 1918 Mr. Rockefeller had funded the lab for six years, a year longer than originally agreed to. Since the state then refused to buy the property or fund the program the buildings were closed. When the State finally bought them five years later, it was because more prison space was needed. The property would never again be used as originally intended.

Although it was in operation only two years, the hospital was carefully evaluated under the aegis of the Bureau of Social Hygiene, a private project of the Rockefellers quite apart from Bedford. Dr. Spaulding's book, *An Experimental Study of Psychopathic Delinquent Women,* was published in 1923. It has since been republished.

While Davis did not, to my knowledge, use the term "moral imbecile," she recognized the symptoms and realized that far more than jailing would be needed to reach them. "There are girls," she wrote, "quite able to do algebra, but totally lacking in any consideration of others, unable to plan ahead, cooperate or work toward goals. They know only this moment's impulse, with no concern whatsoever for its consequences. They have no respect for authority, little empathy for others, and are often overactive."

There are such women here today, more than a few, much the most damaged people here and the furthest from hope of change. I think of a woman who said to me one day in a very conversational tone, "Well ya know, I'm the kinda person minds her own business and don't worry about somebody else. I mean, if there's a woman lying in the next cell dead, I don't give a shit cuz that's the way I am." She said it in a tone that indicated she considered it a character plus, not a flaw.

I was faced one day with a minor emergency and had to call someone within the next fifteen minutes. The woman at the phone had already been talking well beyond the fifteen minutes to which we are asked to limit our phone calls. "Could you try to finish your call soon?" I asked. "I really need to make a call." She looked at me incredulously. "I-don't-care-what-you-need," she said in a Spanish accent, and continued to talk for another twenty minutes. I am naive enough still to be shocked by that.

While the work at Bedford went on, the widely accepted theory about criminals among the general public was that crime sprang across the board from the ranks of those who tested low on intelligence tests.

In an article published in *Good Housekeeping* magazine in 1915, an author wrote:

Speaking of morons (a label chosen from the Greek word for fool), they are born and will breed nothing but defective stock. From this class 7/8 of our criminals are recruited. Take care of the morons, and crime will take care of itself.

Talk of sterilizing "mental defectives" and closing the gates of America to all but "white Anglo-Saxons" was also common at the time. For a while, during the Second World War and the years preceding it, Adolf Hitler made such attitudes unpopular, but they still exist in some circles today in spite of much empirical evidence to the contrary.

To their credit, Davis and others who came to work at the Bedford reformatory were never convinced that low intelligence equated proof of potential criminality. The First World War helped put the notion aside for a while, since all recruits were given intelligence tests, and many who tested low made fine soldiers.

The psychopathic delinquent, referred to by some as the moral imbecile, then as now, is an extremely troubled and troublesome member of society, quite different from the feebleminded. The women singled out for the hospital often tested average, or above average, on a Binet test. It was their emotional control and social skills that were defective. Davis wrote of them, "The dormitory which is suitable for the amenable feebleminded patients, soon became a stage for the histrionic talent of the psychopath. They are misfits wherever they go, in or out of an institution. . . . They are endlessly difficult and often dangerous women who consistently demonstrate serious deviations from acceptable behavior." There are days on my housing unit when I wonder if such women haven't taken over the facility. I wonder, too, if we are not approaching the point where treatment, however expensive, will be less expensive than the cost of neglect. What I'm not sure of is whether there actually is a treatment.

The work of the small hospital at Bedford was highly specialized and extremely expensive, as medical and psychological experimentations usually are. The hospital housed eighteen women at a time, a staff of nine, plus a director, a psychiatrist and a stenographer. (In addition, there were girls from the reformatory who worked in the hospital's kitchen and laundry.) Their work was in the nature of a fact-finding mission.

From its opening, the hospital was never used as a threat or punishment or a place to be disciplined. It was a place to be treated and perhaps educated. Treatment began with improving a woman's physical condition, including persuading her to be treated for syphilis.

Each patient had an individualized program which included several hours in the occupational therapy group, several hours of in- or outdoor planned recreation and an hour of lessons. In other reformatories, it was customary to have two male employees on duty at all times to handle women who grew violent, to put them in handcuffs or jackets or some form of restraint. Here at the hospital, negative discipline was not to be used. Instead, there was an incentive system. There was also a large friendly dog named Tess, that may well have been one of the best therapists there, and I say this without in any way meaning to put down the highly trained people who worked there.

Treatment without force in the care of psychopathic criminals was an untried program then. Every part of the program was designed to motivate the women to use their energy in constructive ways. For a while, doors were even left unlocked and a group feeling of family was encouraged. That didn't work and the doors were soon locked. Discipline usually entailed removal from the group, time spent in "the quiet room," loss of privileges and long comforting warm baths, which proved effective in many instances. At first classes were not required. In a short time no one showed up.

Nurses who had worked in mental hospitals and now came to Bedford to work were shocked by the wide difference between their former patients and the psychopathic delinquents they now saw, their viciousness, their inability to respond to kindness with little more than anger or suspicion.

Dr. Spaulding wrote, "Excitement among our patients was rarely an abnormal condition, but rather the result of lifelong reactions expressed in emotional explosions when any situations in the environment occurred to which it was hard to adjust. Their reactions were (and are) childlike. If they didn't get what they wanted they exploded, and individual crises quickly became group chaos." Many of the women refused to do anything asked of them for the sheer pleasure of starting something. They were children with adult desires and criminal experiences. A woman called "Peachy" on my floor regularly yells, "I do what I wanna do. I'm running this show. I'm the king." Another one, looking straight at a C.O. said, "I can do anything I fuckin' please." Last night a third inmate who had heard something that disturbed her picked up a chair and threw it as hard as she could. She didn't stop to notice that I was on the phone and in the chair's path. And had she noticed, I'm sure she wouldn't have cared. When "Auntie" gets upset she screams obscenities, pulls down her pants and exposes her wide, bare, black bottom to the world at large.

The hope that women who had practiced such habits for a lifetime could be persuaded away from them without some element of force was soon put aside. A disciplinary matron was hired, and she was specifically labeled as such. Even she did not practice the usual mental hospital restraints, nor did the women consider her the ogre one might have expected. For some, she was the source of structure and security they instinctively wanted. With more structure there was more peace and classes were better attended. Repeatedly Spaulding spoke of the need for "a larger and better equipped staff of workers in our prisons and reformatories." The same crying need exists today. Instead the answers I am most frequently given when I ask the reason for a new rule is, "I ain't paid to think. I'm paid to follow directions," or "I don't have to tell you nothin'." There is too much license in some areas, but when attempts to improve are made, the repression is not applied where the license had been. They invariably set the leg that isn't broken. Or they throw away the baby and save the bathwater. Cause and effect seem left out of solutions. The metaphors and the silliness are endless.

Follow-up case histories of the forty-four women treated in the hospital did not indicate any great breakthroughs achieved by the hospital's program. Of those whose lives could be traced after they left Bedford, some turned their lives around with decent jobs or successful marriages, some went back to the same mean streets and habits that would bring them back again to prison. Spaulding's ultimate conclusion was this, "Because of years of undesirable habits of living, no amount of persuasion can bring the individual to her highest level of behavior without some element of force." Not force as retribution, but force as structure.

In Bedford today, in spite of the lessons of sixty-five years ago there is little or no structure for these women to encourage and train new habits. Most of them are placed in the regular population unless and until they do something overt to endanger life and limb, especially the life and limb of a C.O. Their constant need to have their own way and to shriek obscenities if they don't get it are everyday fare. The word seems to be out: "Let 'em yell." When enough inmates grieve certain behavior, the women who yell half the night, set fire repeatedly to their beds and papers, sing in strange ungodly singsong ways for hours at a time, refuse to clean their rooms so that cockroaches proliferate and spread to other cells, are simply moved to a new floor to put other nerves on edge.

Eight

You can't in good conscience teach history anymore, without speaking about women. . . . I keep reminding my students that if women's history were better known we'd have a different story to tell and a different interpretation of traditional categories.

RUTH HARRIS

Katherine Davis straddled two prison eras. She had the missionary zeal and optimism of an early reformer, and the drive and working intellect of the Chairman of the Board. Her tenure at Bedford lasted through the height of what is remembered historically as the "Progressive Period." By then many of the women entering prisons to do good deeds were working for pay. Many were single or divorced. They were highly politicized and supported women's suffrage. Their attitude toward the incarcerated woman was definitely beginning to change. They talked less about the "moral superiority" of women, and more about medical, sociological and educational needs and mental deficiency. The words of the popular music at the time still insisted little girls were sugar and spice and everything nice, but then getting everybody on the same wavelength in the short span of twenty years is next to impossible. There's always a front and a back, the beginning and the end of any parade.

Before Davis left Bedford, a big change was already apparent in the women and girls coming to the Bedford reformatory. There were more social services available to girls and women, so those who might have been sentenced to a reformatory for want of a better alternative could now turn elsewhere for help. Immigrant protective leagues, the YWCA, Big Sisters, Florence Crittendon homes, the National Council of Jewish Women, the Junior League and others were reaching out to help. Police women with social casework experience were beginning to serve women in city jails, though even then many of the jails were little better than Newgate had been.

In 1908 a separate women's night court was established in New York City so that women charged with prostitution and loitering were taken there and put in the hands of women to be fingerprinted and checked for venereal disease. Members of the Women's Prison Association were often there to pay fines for them so they wouldn't have to turn to their pimps for help. In the meantime, the Association lobbied for an end to such fines. For a while the fines were abolished, but they returned.

While a fine and bail are not the same, lack of the money to pay either one results in jail time for the poor.

Today at Rikers Island in New York City, which incidentally is now the largest jail compound in the world, approximately 50 percent of the women (and men too) are awaiting trial or waiting to plea-bargain. They can't leave because they can't raise the money for bail, though for many bail may be set as low as a few hundred dollars. Sister Vincentia, one of the wonderful nuns who monthly drives a van of children from the far end of Long Island to Bedford Hills to see their mothers, was called recently to come and post bail for a woman who had already been in jail two weeks because she couldn't raise $75. She had eight children waiting for her outside.

In 1913 Davis was asked to become the commissioner of Corrections for the City of New York. *The New York Times* had one word to describe its opinion of the selection—"appalling." "Handling the hardened criminal," it added, "is a man's job." The University of Chicago was justly proud of its graduate and its magazine featured a glowing article about Dr. K. B. Davis, though it also wondered what Mayor-elect John P. Mitchell might have had in mind when he made the appointment. The *Brooklyn Eagle* (was it the *Village Voice* of its day?) wrote, "It is the appointment of a prison executive who has conspicuously 'made good' in her own field. . . . It is an effort to secure the application of modern methods in our city prisons and reformatories in place of the medieval systems which has brought about the scandals in the Tombs and in Blackwells Island in the past year. We seem to be at the door to a period of prison house-cleaning. . . . No administrative change is more needed than this." And who better to do the housecleaning than a woman?

Davis's first day on the job, she made an official visit to Blackwells Island. As they neared the dock, she saw women in gray stripes scrambling over a coal barge that was being unloaded. "You cannot reform a woman who is wearing bed-ticking," she said. "I shall order the women prisoners' clothes to be made of neat, pretty gingham." Unfortunately, she soon discovered an inventory of eighteen thousand yards of stripes, so the change took a while. Since then, of course, the likes of Bill Blass and Albert Nippon have made some great clothes with bed-ticking, but they're more fun when you have a little variety and you can pick the moment you wear them.

One of Davis's first acts was to have two of her investigators get themselves arrested and sentenced to three weeks in the Tombs. They quickly discovered what had been whispered about for a long time. With enough money to bribe the right people you could get put in an "all white" cell and get something other than prison food—at twice the price you'd pay at the Waldorf. For $5 you could get a spot where you might observe and take part in the drug and alcohol trade. No amount of money was too large to ask or too small to accept. If you only had a nickel, you bought a nickel's worth of privilege.

Though I'm sure there were still ways around it, and God knows there are today, Davis sent out a strong order that there were to be no more privileges at the Tombs or Blackwells Island—every cell was to be integrated, and no more food and tobacco could be sent in. A newspaper commented, "Going to prison in Gotham will be a more serious proposition than it has been for many a long day. . . . If this is feminism, let us have more of it."

Davis's edicts were understandably unpopular with many prisoners. She took office on January 2, 1914. On July 8, 1914, a young inmate at the Tombs, member of the Industrial Workers of the World, "brilliant in mind, if erratic in his youthful spirit," sprang to his feet and said, "We'll riot!"

While the prisoners were revving up for a riot, Katherine Davis was attending a conference at the estate of Mrs. O. H. P. Belmont in Newport. The two honored guests were Katherine Davis and the Duchess of Marlborough. Again, it is the *University of Chicago Magazine* that assures us Katherine was the hit of the meeting and "kept her audience laughing." She said, "In New York, which is one hundred years behind the times, we have penitentiaries in which no one is penitent, reformatories which do not reform, and houses of corrections which do not correct." That may have been a laugh-getter in 1914, but in 1988 it's still true and it's no joke.

Davis left her meeting quickly, having been offered the use of one of her hostess's boats, and arrived at the Tombs with the riot in full swing. A newspaper next day wrote, "The lady Commissioner donned her best dress, seized her parasol and went forth to quell the riot." Davis said, "I did not have a parasol."

I have seen only one picture of Katherine Davis, a poor copy of a newspaper picture. She was standing at Grand Central Station next to President Harding and several others: tall, wrapped in a winter coat and furs and wearing a huge beribboned hat so little of her face was visible. In my mind's eye she looked not unlike Miss Lake, the headmistress of Laurel School, my alma mater, tall, imposing, and not a little formidable, but a twinkle all the same.

As long as the riot and attendant unrest lasted, Davis worked in the office of Warden Hays, refusing to let others do what she considered her job. She would stay, she promised, not only until the insurrection ended, but until she knew all the causes of it.

Quiet was finally restored. The first time all the prisoners returned to the dining room she stood at the doorway with the warden and looked each prisoner straight in the eye. No one spoke. At the end of the first week, Davis herself conducted the prison's Protestant services and attended the Jewish and Catholic ones as well.

Soon after the riot, she was quoted as saying, "Criminals are not only *like* bad boys. The *are* bad boys. They are strong individualists. So are children. . . . Social consciousness is asleep in the criminal as it is in the child. In both it must be awakened, and after it is awakened, trained."

Perhaps I am too old to judge that statement objectively, but I find it very wise. There are many men and women in prison today who are the grandchildren and great grandchildren of those Davis worked with, who somehow never heard "those homely truths which they could comprehend." I wish so often that top administrators would sit down frequently with small groups here and listen and talk in simple homilies on folksy subjects which many of us remember through a lifetime. Something as simple as suggesting, "When you go to the gym to hear a program of any sort, don't talk during it and don't wander aimlessly around the room." "When you talk with a friend find a place other than a doorway to chat." "When you have been on the phone for half an hour and twenty other women need it, too, don't tell the C.O. to go fuck himself when he asks you to say goodbye." There is simple logic in these suggestions, but they aren't logical to people who have spent a lifetime grabbing to get something and fighting to keep it. I heard a woman in the hall say to another, "I don't give a fuck about your feelings." Prisons do not change that attitude. Punishment, as Davis believed, should fit the criminal, not the crime. Instead, today all are thrown into the same pot and nothing in the stew is properly digested by anyone. All are treated like mentally deficient children. "Do this, do that. No, no, no, not that, like this." "It's your own fault. You brought it on yourself." "You didn't do it the way I wanted you to. Now go back and do it again." This is not what develops maturity. It only nourishes hatred. "The nature of the crime a criminal commits," Davis wrote, "is largely determined by the accidents of opportunity — of circumstances — environment and association. Some who are punished and set free are as dangerous after punishment as they were before. Some who might be truly reformed are more harmed than helped by the operation of the present punitive system."

The *Union Advertiser*, in July 1914, wrote, "K. B. Davis is giving a very noble exhibition of how a municipal department should be managed, and those who believe the franchise should be extended to women have every reason to point to her with pardonable pride." It took six more years, and a good deal of marching, but in 1920, along with all the other female citizens of the United States, this brilliant woman finally cast her first vote. It would be twenty years after her death before a woman could serve on a federal jury.

After two years as commissioner, Davis took the position of chairman of the Parole Commission and served for three years. From 1918 to 1928 she was general secretary of the Bureau of Social Hygiene of the Rockefeller Foundation, where her deep concern for the problems of prostitutes and prostitution were again given her primary energies.

For the rest of her life, Davis tried to teach and interest people in what she had learned about female criminality in her studies at Bedford. She gave many speeches and wrote many articles to help the public understand these women and to know that many were indeed mental defectives who had not gone wrong out of perversity but out of an inability to think clearly and understand the consequences of their actions.

Katherine Davis died in 1935. John D. Rockefeller, Jr. said of her, "She was the cleverest woman I ever met."

Nine

Punishment pains man, but does not make him better.

NIETZSCHE

Davis left a difficult act to follow, and a more difficult setting in which to follow it. A woman named Mary Harris who had been studying at the University of Chicago while Davis was there followed her as superintendent of the reformatory. It had already become apparent before Davis left that something more than missing dessert would be necessary to handle the new group of women coming in. Davis herself had permitted handcuffing some women to their beds. After a particularly loud and rough disturbance at meals one evening, Harris imposed a rule of silence during meals. It smacked too much of the men's penitentiaries. She was roundly criticized in the media and the women raised hell.

Davis was quick to defend her. A *New York Post* article of July 13, 1915 was headlined, "Katherine Davis combats Muckrakers. They debate all day at the Workhouse." It had then become popular in some circles to drop the term reformatory and apply the name Bedford Workhouse instead. Davis, who had run the reformatory for thirteen years in very much the way early headmistresses had first run their domains—as a majority of one with complete control, had little use for the interference of outsiders. "Miss Harris," she answered the press, "can be trusted to work with the weak-willed for their good. . . . Women who give every promise of worth under restraint, but who surrender to alcohol and drugs when set free, crowd the workhouse. Salvaging human derelicts," she explained, "and putting lawbreakers back into the class of decent men and women is a heavy responsibility."

Almost immediately Harris was faced with growing problems of racism, as more and more blacks arrived, and the reformatory now held one hundred more women than it could properly care for.

In 1915 the New York Board of Charities was appointed to investigate charges of racial problems made against the reformatory, the first but not the last investigation in the facility's history. Some suggested segregation on campus as the answer. Some suggested two entirely separate institutions as the answer.

Many now criticized Davis's earlier policy of integration and claimed that was one of the problems. What troubled many the most they found awkward to talk about without hiding behind euphemisms. The truth was, some of the white women were finding some of the black women sexually appealing. They still do. Homosexuality had existed right from the start but not to the extent that overcrowding made possible and the mixture of races made it a cause célèbre.

The final report of the investigation stated ambiguously, "While the committee makes no objection to integrated cottages because of the color line, it is undoubtedly true that the most undesirable sex relations grow out of this mingling of the two races."

106

In 1916 ostensibly "at the request of the black women," two new cottages were built "for blacks only." From that time until the end of the 1950s, there was segregation of the races here at Bedford: separate housing, separate kitchen, separate dining. The segregated dining building built in 1939, when the cottage kitchens were closed, is used today as the staff dining hall. When built, whites ate on the first floor and blacks ate on a lower floor. It's a basement today—what they called it then I don't know. When I arrived here in 1981, there was still a faded sign over the basement lavatory reading, For Blacks Only. It has been painted over.

It is ironic how quick Americans are to damn apartheid in South Africa, and to forget how recently we supported our own apartheid, a gentler version possibly, but, philosophically, apartheid and segregation are essentially the same. We've pretty well laid to rest the "separate but equal" myth. Giving us different colored skins and different facial characteristics and the ability to reproduce ourselves so easily were among the hardest tests God created for us. We are still struggling mightily with them and probably will until the day we make ourselves extinct.

The Board of Charities strongly endorsed segregation, better food for the women, more recreational opportunities, and urged that in the future judges send "fewer mental defectives" to Bedford. "Put them in asylums instead." Today we are philosophically torn about whether they belong in mental institutions, prisons or on the streets. Life is much simpler for bigots.

By the time America entered the First World War, Harris had left Bedford and Helen Cobb was superintendent. The war played an important part in nudging the basic purpose of women's prisons away from reformation of women and toward the preserva-

107

tion of society. The benevolent attitude toward women in reformatories had begun to fade away. Protecting our fighting men was the first priority. A federal report estimated that by imprisoning a prostitute it saved the $7 it cost to treat each infected man, at the expense of 11¢ per prevented sexual encounter. However it may have arrived at these figures, they were convincing enough to send thousands of prostitutes to jails and prisons, wherever there was room for them. They were rounded up under the auspices of the Committee on Training Camp Activities. The prostitute, so recently "the victim," was now the social threat. The courts clung to the concept that women were reformable, however, because it served to legitimize giving women longer sentences for the same crimes men committed. The longer sentences continued to be filed under "special consideration."

In 1919, a new investigation at Bedford was made, prompted by a former inmate's charging cruel and unusual punishment was being used there. "Women," she charged, "are being handcuffed to doors or walls so their toes barely touch the ground — and some are cuffed and their faces pushed into cold water." The young ladies who had "joyfully" pushed wheelbarrows up and down the campus hills were long gone. While only first offenders had been sent to Bedford Hills at first, now 60 percent were recidivists, 75 percent were practicing prostitutes when arrested, 70 percent had venereal diseases, 16 percent were psychopaths and many others needed custodial care.

Al Smith was governor at the time and it was he who ordered the inquiry. "If such things as are reported in the papers are going on I will take immediate steps to have them stopped." Superintendent Helen Cobb was called as a witness and admitted that girls were handcuffed to a door or wall, "but never with their feet off the floor." She admitted their faces were sometimes dipped in water, "dipped, never dunked," and that the girls were sometimes fed bread and water because "this benefits the girls and helps in maintaining discipline." The water was only used when a girl was excited or hysterical. "The use of water is not considered discipline," she said, "it is considered treatment." One girl testified she was cuffed to her door for three days and fed bread and water, still cuffed.

As the investigation went on, a matron testified she had seen girls handcuffed and given the water treatment more than one hundred separate times. "In some cases the girls looked near dead when it was over . . . when the handcuffs came off a girl couldn't speak. She was left in a cell without a bed, so she slept on the floor." Another matron testified some girls were cuffed for refusing to leave the dining room, because they hadn't had enough to eat.

The only near riot I have come close to being part of was over leaving the dining room, too. One of the sergeants had suddenly instituted a new, far more regimented procedure for mealtime. The word went out, "When you've finished eating don't leave. We're having a sit-in." When the C.O.s realized what we were doing they wasted no time at all dragging in fire hoses and threatening to turn them on anyone who didn't leave at once. We all left—but some of the women continued the argument on their floors, refusing to go to their cells. They were all given charge sheets and later, after much discussion and waste of time and money, the charge sheets were withdrawn because someone in authority had followed the wrong procedures in issuing them. It bends the mind to imagine the litigation that might follow if a woman today were left cuffed to the door, her toes barely touching the ground. Yet, today it is still socially acceptable to handcuff and chain her when taking her to the hospital, even in the final stages of labor. Sandy underwent a six-hour operation on her spine and came to chained to her bed. She was later given clemency. Obviously, it took a while to decide whether she was too dangerous to be operated on without chains or responsible enough to be let out as a good citizen, which she has certainly proved to be.

A member of the Board of Managers, when questioned under oath, admitted the water "treatment" was not administered under the advice of a doctor. "But it did subdue them and cause them to behave better in the future."

A Mrs. Hoffman, head matron, testified that the girls found the handcuffs "soothing" and that they were necessary during withdrawal from drugs. Today most, if not all, women who come to Bedford have been through the worst of withdrawal before they arrive. Getting to prison is usually a long, drawn-out affair.

Stories were also told at the hearing of girls being forced to shovel coal three hours at a time, and to take on still other tasks too heavy for them. This didn't raise eyebrows as it would today because at the time child labor laws, where they had been passed, had been declared unconstitutional. New York had passed a law in 1893 limiting a working shift in certain industries to ten hours—but it was loosely enforced. States competed with one another for business and each was loath to pass a child labor law that would give the other states a competitive advantage. Illinois, in 1893, went so far as to limit women to an eight-hour working day, but that law, too, was thrown out as unconstitutional since it "deprived people of income without due process."

The U.S. Supreme Court's decision that a New York law limiting bakers to a ten-hour day, because of the excessive heat, was unconstitutional was the first state social legislation to be so declared by the High Court.

It is doubtful if the newspaper-reading public was very upset by the news of sixteen- to thirty-year-old "delinquents" having to shovel coal for three hours at a time. The industrial revolution had taken millions of very young children out of their homes and into the work force. By the beginning of the twentieth century, 2.25 million children under fifteen were working full time in mills, mines and factories and as house servants on twenty-four-hour call. Children as young as four were kept sixteen hours a day rolling cigars. Five-year-olds worked the night shift in cotton mills.

We've largely graduated from infant servitude now—except in the field of pornography—but the problem of where to get a large supply of cheap labor is still with us. The president's wanting to lower the minimum wage "so more young people can get jobs" is the thinking of those who have no concept of poverty.

While different versions were given of just how inhumane work and discipline at Bedford had become, all agreed that discipline had now become a serious problem because of two groups growing larger all the time, the mentally deficient and the "just plain naughty."

Most witnesses defended Superintendent Cobb as only doing what had to be done, though one girl testified that Cobb hit her with a bunch of keys. The keys snarled in her hair and Cobb had proceeded to drag her around the hall five times by the hair. One matron, asked if a girl with a weak heart should be so treated, answered, "Any girl who can break windows and swear like these do, doesn't have a heart problem." Some of the medical decisions in prison today are still that scientific. "We'll take a look at the blood clot in your leg," they told Shelly, "after you pick up your stuff and move to 114A & B."

Early in February 1920, while the investigation was still in progress, a woman named Evelyn was locked in segregation because she refused to salute the flag. The papers reported it. Superintendent Cobb was defended in this move by the Board of Managers.

I'm sure I'd have been equally shocked and perhaps done what Cobb did. By the time I graduated from high school in 1941, I had pledged allegiance to the flag every school day of my life. I couldn't imagine anyone wanting not to. It was part of the ritual of life. Yet only two years later, in 1943, the Supreme Court decided that citizens couldn't be forced to salute the flag.

As a result of the investigation of 1920-1921, handcuffing and the water treatment were to be stopped at once, a full-time psychiatrist was to be added to the staff, the education programs were to be expanded and the institution was henceforth to be directly responsible to the State Department of Correction, rather than a Board of Managers. The board would now have a consulting role instead of managerial role.

By the end of February 1920, Superintendent Cobb had resigned saying, "I think I can lead a more congenial life doing something else." A ladylike exit if ever I heard one.

Julia Monique was named acting head. During her short stay, the media announced that Bedford girls were sent out to work as domestics or farmhands in the local neighborhood and their wages were kept by the institution. Monique explained that the girls and women were often paroled to a family that agreed to have them come and work for them as domestic servants. It was called "the indenture system" by the reformatory in Framingham, Massachusetts, where the system was first introduced. An inmate could accept the contract or stay in prison. Once she had accepted it, running away was a criminal offense, and if she ran and was found, she was returned to the reformatory. Her salary, depending upon the generosity of her employer, was anywhere from $1.50 to $2.50 per week. There was nothing like a minimum wage in those days, and many young women, never arrested, earned little more. When the girls were paroled, Monique explained, a trust fund was set up for them. Part of their earnings were put into it so when their parole periods ended they would have a small "nest egg" to start life anew. I have a friend in here today who was here at the reformatory in the late 1950s. Each workday morning, she and other women boarded a facility truck and were driven to a neighboring farm to work for the day. When she was finally paroled, there was no "trust" fund to go with her, nor was there one later on. The whole story of prison finance, yesterday or today, will never be told—will probably never even be known.

In March 1920, the next superintendent, Florence Jones, was appointed. With the list of needed improvements to go by, she broadened the educational offerings, in particular current events, though newspapers were still not allowed on campus. News of the outside was considered too worldly and shocking for girls to read. In the men's prisons, they had long been permitted. At one of the current events sessions, Jones announced that Representative Warren G. Harding had been nominated for the presidency. The girls, for some reason, clapped enthusiastically. Superintendent Jones wrote to Mr. Harding to tell him. He wrote back a kind letter and thanked her very much.

Under Superintendent Jones, discipline was much modified, far less harsh than it had been. But on July 25, 1920, four months after Jones's appointment, a race riot broke out at Bedford. It started in the laundry between a black girl and a white girl and soon spread, with sides chosen by color. One hundred and fifty women took part, fighting with knives, clubs and flatirons. According to *The New York Times,* they were "clubbed into submission," after holding twenty-five state troopers and the Bedford Police Department at bay. The police criticized the "modified disciplinary measures" that had been adopted on the strength of the recent inquiry. Three days later Ms. Jones resigned, saying she couldn't do the job if she weren't permitted to use "reasonable discipline." Even the institution's Catholic chaplain publicly demanded a return to "sterner measures."

Four days after the riot was subdued, Governor Smith came to Bedford to visit the reformatory. The women were told in advance that he was coming in the hope that his interest would settle them down. It was wishful thinking. More than a hundred women crowded to the windows and yelled, screamed and jeered, "What the hell do we care for the governor?" Two days later, a *New York Times* editorial commented, "It wouldn't have taken a mental giant to figure out that it was to the girls' best interest to be courteous to the Governor."

What was perhaps not yet apparent then, but could be listed as a prime characteristic of many female inmates today, is their unawareness of or lack of concern for their own best interests, an inability to think far enough ahead to know what their best interests may be. What they know is right now—what I feel like doing, what I feel like yelling, what I feel like wanting. How they would react to a visit by Governor Cuomo I don't know. They would probably be courteous. If Reagan came they'd throw rocks or maybe just tear the whole place apart. They don't know much about him except that they hate him.

Once again, an interim head was chosen, this

114

time from the Board of Managers, in the person of Mrs. Frank Christian. She let rioters go back to cottages, extended the field of current events study and permitted the girls to have writing paper and pencils. "They can write all they want," she said. An inmate newspaper was also begun, probably not unlike the present one, which is all sweetness and light and clearly states that it is produced by the education department, not the inmates. Superintendent Christian authorized an increase of three-fourths of a pound of sugar per week per woman and larger portions of food. This meant eight thousand pounds more per year of sugar. The amount of sugar consumed here today must be astronomic. It is not unusual to see a woman put six or eight teaspoons of sugar in one cup of coffee. I am told this has something to do with the addictive personality—a search for a substitute. Christian asked the public to write the girls, to give them contact with upstanding people in the outside world.

After a search of several months, Mrs. Anna Talbot took over as regular superintendent. She announced at an interview that "kindly firmness" would not be her style, but, rather, "firmly kindness." Whichever it was, it didn't work. She lasted five months and then resigned, too—in the face of a strong recommendation from Albany. At this point Albany, having heard as much as it wanted to about the reformatory in Bedford, took a drastic step. In 1921 it amended the legislation that had established the reformatory so that a man could now be made superintendent. The job of superintendent was consolidated with that of psychiatrist. Dr. Amos Baker, psychiatrist, took over the office of superintendent saying he would be "lenient but firm." He added, "I believe many of the inmates are psychopathic cases and I will use every scientific method possible to help this class of girls."

115

Twenty years would go by and six men would run the institution before a woman was again appointed. Her name was Henrietta Addition. The year was 1940.

Dr. Baker spent most of his energies at Bedford giving mental tests to classify prisoners according to their mentality in an effort to find out which of the more serious troublemakers were mentally irresponsible and which were deliberately malicious, or as Spaulding had put it, which were mental defectives and which were psychopathic delinquents.

But while Dr. Baker was studying brains, no one with ultimate authority was minding the store. Women who had been hired as "matrons," not prison guards, who dressed all in white as nurses, and would do so for another forty years, were being forced into situations they were totally untrained to handle. While one of them left "the girls" in the yard to "go and get her shawl" one evening, ten Bedford girls escaped into the woods. Angered because many of their friends had been labeled "defective" and moved to special housing, some of those left behind started to riot. Headlines in a New York paper on June 24, 1921 read, "Bedford in Tumult Under Rule of Man." Five months later, in the Hartford, Connecticut *Times,* members of the American Bar Association law enforcement committee said, "Women banded together as prison reformers are too sentimental about criminals, are responsible for creating crime waves." What we need, they said, is "real punishment." They didn't define it.

Ten

All that we know who lie in jail
is that the wall is strong.

OSCAR WILDE,
THE BALLAD OF READING GAOL

By 1930, the country was in the slough of a depression and all spending, public and private, was affected. The decision was made that two women's prisons in the state was one prison too many, so Auburn Prison for Women was permanently closed and all the women who had been incarcerated there were transferred, by heavily guarded train and bus, to Bedford Hills. While we think of poverty as one of the main causes of crime, our jails and prisons were not filled to overflowing during the 1930s. The prison crush of prohibition was over, and nothing like it would happen again until "the second prohibition" which we are, of course, living through now.

A commission appointed in 1931 to investigate crime and punishment in the United States, announced in its final report, "The prisons of our nation are a failure. They're outworn and inhumane." That same year a new prison was opened in upstate

New York at Attica. It was heralded with this headline, "New Prison at Attica to be Convicts Paradise." Forty years later, it was the scene of the worst prison riot in our history. Like the first warden at Newgate, we still have a tendency to jump too fast to be self-congratulatory about our prisons.

The women from Auburn were housed across the street from the reformatory where Rockefeller's laboratory and psychopathic hospital had been. The two facilities, prison and reformatory, were to be completely self-sufficient and separate from one another, except for a shared superintendent. The name of the combined facilities was Westfield State Farm. Extensive building was done during the 1930s on both sides of the road. On the reformatory grounds, building included a new administration building, staff rooms, storehouse, laundry, a complete medical center and a dining room-kitchen building named "the segregation building," since blacks and whites ate in separate areas. The latter building was finished in 1939, under the federal Works Program Administration. What caused the federal government to foot the bill for a state prison I'm not sure, but President Franklin D. Roosevelt is given due credit on a large brass plaque inside the building. Money was also appropriated to remodel the former Laboratory of Social Hygiene to make it usable as a prison.

A woman named Ruth Brown was the first person to enter Bedford prison when the move from Auburn took place. She was issued the ID number 31-G-001 and held it for fifty-three years until her death in 1984. She had been condemned to death, along with her husband, for murder. He was electrocuted. Ruth lived on death row at Sing Sing for months. Her head was shaved and she was headed for electrocution when her sentence was commuted to life.

She was living in the prison nursery when I ar-

118

rived here in 1981 and known to everyone then as "Granny" or "Ma." She had been paroled by Governor Thomas Dewey, stayed out for ten years, and then requested to come back in as a parole violator. She was drinking heavily, and she had spent so much of her life in prison by then she could never adjust to the outside. I couldn't understand that seven years ago. I can today. When Ma's parole hearings came up periodically, she simply refused to go to them. Whether that could still be done today, I don't know. I know one woman who served fourteen years, went out and came back begging to be let back in. She was for awhile. I know two women who fought to stay in, at least until their "woman" went out, too. As one of them explained, "You don't know what it's like out there with nobody."

As long as the prison and reformatory were designated as two separate units, women in them were to be kept totally segregated. But some contact between the two was inevitable, especially if a prison inmate had a baby, because the nursery was on the reformatory side of the road. Since the closing of Mt. Pleasant in Ossining, only women in State reformatories could keep babies born during their incarceration with them in prison for the baby's first year. In 1930, through the efforts of many women's groups, a bill was introduced and passed into law permitting women in New York State prisons as well as reformatories to have their babies brought back to prison with them. The bill was signed into law by then governor of New York, Franklin Delano Roosevelt. It is still on the books as law 611.

Provided the medical department and superintendent of the facility found no reason for the child not to stay, a baby could remain in the facility for one year or for eighteen months if the mother was going out in that period of time. But staying for the full year was not encouraged. The nursery was thought of as a safe haven for the child until permanent housing could be arranged with family, a foster home or with an adoptive family. More of the babies were adopted then than today, partly because motherhood without marriage was still not looked upon as benignly as it is today, and a mother's civil rights and parental rights were not of particular public concern. Studies of bonding between mother and child were barely beginning, and it is only within the past fifteen years that they have begun to be considered important enough to take seriously.

There is little concern expressed anywhere in the early readings I have done about mother and child relationships or efforts to bring children to visit their mothers. It is only in the past fifteen years that the facility has expressed this as one of its priorities. Barbara, a friend of mine presently incarcerated here, was two years old when she came with her father, uncle and grandmother to visit her mother in 1950. She was kept in an anteroom with a matron until the visit between the adults was finished. If the right matron was on duty, she was slipped quietly into the place where her mother sat and permitted to visit for a few minutes. Other times she was not allowed in at all.

As long as the prison remained separate from the reformatory, a mother on the prison side could see her baby only twice a week unless she was nursing it, and then special arrangements were made. The rest of the time it was cared for by one of the reformatory mothers. When the two facilities were finally incorporated into one in 1970, administrative philosophy in the nursery took a 180 degree turn. Now, instead of requiring mothers to get quickly back to work, which is certainly the most constructive approach for young mothers in poverty, they are virtually forced to remain in the nursery except when an approved sitter is found. Getting approved as a sitter today is a little like getting Senate approval to become a member of the Supreme Court — sometimes harder. So much times goes by while the candidate's name sits on the counselor's desk, then the head counselor's desk, then the deputy superintendent of programs and then the deputy superintendent of security, she often gives up and classifies into another job. Sometimes she is even paroled before the decision is made. I can only suppose that the constant fear of litigation causes this, unless, of course, it's simple neglect.

It must have been complicated trying to remember which rules applied to the reformatory and which to the prison. It's almost impossible to keep track of them today when the same rules apply to all inmates. Someone is always shuffling papers trying to find an old memo to refresh the memory of one of the powers that be, who can't remember what he or she last said.

The rules that applied to the women's prison did not usually apply to the reformatory. And the rules that applied to men's prisons did not necessarily apply to the women's prison. All the rule books for corrections officers, until the end of the 1960s, used only the masculine pronoun, but that wasn't unusual. According to Phyllis Baunach, who has studied women's prisons and written extensively about them, the massive ten-volume report issued in 1967 by the President's Commission on Law Enforcement and the Administration of Justice made not one mention of women offenders.

The women who served the C.O. function at Bedford were called "matrons," and wore white nurses' uniforms and were paid less than the men for exactly the same duties. While it is now acknowledged that women do go to prison in New York State, the fact is still often forgotten. As late as 1983, the official package-room list issued to me said I was allowed to have two jockstraps and two hundred cigars per month. Nowhere did it list a brassiere or lipstick.

We know, from a pamphlet printed to advertise for new matrons in 1956, that "no specialized training or experience" was required — only an elementary Civil Service exam and the following qualifications: "age 21, good moral character and habits, free from any mental or physical defect that would have a tendency to incapacitate; must be physically proportioned within the range of accepted standards, and have satisfactory hearing and eyesight." A Wasserman test was also required. "Conviction of a felony *will* bar, and conviction of a misdemeanor may bar, appointment." A high school equivalency diploma fulfilled educational requirements, and even this could be waived if the candidate was a mother or foster mother of "school age girls." It leaves one wondering what the author of these requirements thought of the average teenage girl. Except for the waiver of a diploma if you have a school-age daughter, the requirements to become a corrections officer are essentially the same today, plus six weeks academy training and six weeks "on the job" training.

Unfortunately, whatever is learned at the academy does not do much to prepare a C.O. to take over a prison post. It is not unusual for the inmate unit clerk on the floor to join new C.O.s in the officer's bubble to show them how to open and close doors, to show them the difference between A corridor and B corridor, to explain about sign-up sheets, to whom and when to issue a blue pass, when the hall door should be open and when it should be closed, etc., etc. I suppose the confusion is one of the reasons one often hears a C.O. say, "We're gonna do it *my* way," thus obviating the need to find out what is the official procedure. There's a case to be made for this, since whatever official procedure is this week it's bound to be different next week. And logic won't help you to remember.

A matron's duties in the 1950s and 1960s far exceeded the requirements to be hired. They were listed as these:

DUTIES: Under general supervision the matron acts as custodian of female inmates of a state prison or reformatory and supervises their activities and conduct; and does related work as required. Example (Illustrative only): Maintaining order and discipline; guarding against injury to persons or to property; making decisions in emergency situations; recognizing and modifying antisocial behavior; taking precautions to prevent disturbances and escapes by discouraging undesirable habits, by encouraging group programs and by good counsel; assigning and supervising work of inmates; checking the inmates in and out of work and classes; teaching housekeeping, food preparation, mending and related activities to inmates; writing reports of conduct and progress of inmates; requisitioning, issuing, condemning, and taking inventories of clothing and supplies.

A 1939 booklet entitled, *Rules and Regulations Governing Inmates of the New York State Penal Institutions,* gives one a flavor of the life of a prison inmate. There were three "grades" of inmates. New inmates were all first grade, and wore white discs on the left sleeve to so signify. Parole violators were second grade and wore blue discs. Anyone who had attempted to escape was third grade, and wore a red disc. Each year one remained a first grader she or he was presented with a bar or some mark of distinction. If you lost your white disc you could never get another one. You could earn back first-grade standing in six months' time—but never the white disc. Instead, you were given a white circle. It was a little like losing one's virginity. You couldn't do it twice.

First-grade prisoners had privileges which, though limited, left them far better off than second- or third-grade prisoners. They could write as many letters as the warden approved. They were given one stamp per month and all letters in and out were read. First-grade prisoners could also receive newspapers and magazines if they came directly from the publisher, and have a one-hour visit from relatives once a week. The entire brochure was still written as though no females were involved. "No female visitors shall be permitted to visit inmates except members of the immediate family." A friend other than a female could visit once a month with the warden's permission. There was no suggestion that the opposite was true for women.

Second-grade inmates could have relatives visit once every two weeks, write a letter twice a month and get no magazines or newspapers without special permission of the warden. Third graders had a visit or wrote a letter only with the hard-won permission of the warden. Visits for all men on Sundays and holidays required special written permission which was mailed to the visitor and had to be brought with the visitor for admittance. Commissary purchases could be made weekly by first graders, every other week by second graders, and not at all by third graders, unless the warden, for some special reason, gave permission. A similar hierarchy exists today.

124

Fiske residents shop every week, regular population shops every other week and women in SHU have no commissary privileges at all.

A kind of thinking that prefers taking privileges away from inmates to having them earned still prevails today in New York State. A woman or man entering prison is given "good time," that is, time off the back of her or his maximum sentence. By misbehaving, they can lose their privileges, but no amount of good behavior will give them more. Every state in the Union, with two exceptions, works merit time the other way. The inmate works to earn merit time, thus motivating better behavior and efforts at personal rehabilitation.

Male inmates in 1939 marched to meals "with military step into and out of the mess hall." While in their cells, "silence must be observed at all times. Talking, laughing, reading aloud, shuffling of feet, drawing a chair across cell floor or calling from cell to cell is strictly prohibited." The latter was less strict for women than for men but, for all, lights were out at 9:00 P.M.

Wearing uniforms in the women's prison was an on-again, off-again thing as it still is. When I arrived here I was issued similar jumpers in yellow, blue and green. Blue quickly became contraband. Then the yellow was taken away, though now we can wear yellow shirts and sweaters if they are sent from outside. The 1939 rule book indicated uniforms were required. A woman could wear her own underwear, socks, shirts and sweaters in white or gray. Today, anything gray is contraband.

No jewelry was allowed except a watch. Money then, as now, was contraband. All bartering among inmates was forbidden, and you couldn't pay others to do your maintenance work for you. Notes from one prisoner to another were forbidden. Today we are allowed two necklaces and three pairs of ear-rings, but we can't wear them in the visiting room, the only place that matters. Women are permitted to sell their knitting to outsiders or inmates, all exchanges subject to approval and done through commissary disbursement sheets.

All outside contacts were obviously discouraged, even to the extent that, "Gazing at visitors or strangers passing through the prison is strictly forbidden." It was still shades of the Auburn system. To the best of my knowledge, these rules prevailed for the men for another thirty years. The women were allowed to talk, but any obscenity or rude remark was, we're told, punished. We're still told that, but it isn't true.

In the years just preceding the Second World War, women had changed and some penal techniques had changed, too. The starry-eyed reformers of the early twentieth century were less starry-eyed. Rural and domestic values were being replaced by urban standards instead, and more and more blacks were coming to prison.

By 1941 the war had made us cautious enough so that those who now came to visit the male prisoners had to be fingerprinted first, in duplicate with one copy forwarded to the division of criminal identification for a search, and one copy kept at the facility. "No person shall be permitted to visit pending a report on such search."

The rule book added such procedures did not apply to "spiritual advisors, lawyers, or immediate family at Westfield State Farm, or facilities for the mentally deficient." On a number of different publications from the Department of Corrections, Westfield was listed on a separate page along with all the facilities for the mentally deficient. What the connection was must be left to the reader's imagination. My favorite rule in the 1941 rule book, paragraph

126

181, provided that "only one person will occupy a cell at a time while undergoing solitary confinement or isolation." One could only wish to find more such clear thinking in the corrections system.

In 1958 Bedford again made the headlines. War and peace were no longer front page news, and the economy was in good shape. It was harder to find a good story so the papers dug deeper. An April 1958 headline read, "Irregularities Found in Bedford Women's Prison." "Some women staff members and inmates of Westfield State Farm women's correctional institution are engaging in homosexual practices." I feel almost a sense of nostalgia for the days when this was considered news. (A gang rape, two weeks ago, of Bedford inmates by five other Bedford inmates was barely considered worth reporting.) The article continued that there was maltreatment of inmates by some guards and "sloppy administration."

The Commissioner of Corrections, Thomas Murphy, was quoted as saying, "We absolutely will not tolerate any such thing. If we get the slightest hint of any such thing, we investigate right away." Weeks later, Governor Averell Harriman announced, "An investigation was held. We haven't been able to obtain enough information to take action." A familiar story still.

On April 2, 1958, the headlines read, "Prison Cottages Fire Traps . . . Staff Morale Reported Low." Matrons' salaries started at $3,500 that year, which was a little less than I was earning that year as a teacher with twelve years experience. It was also less than men in male prisons earned for doing the same work. The newspaper added, "Little effort is made to check the staff background, and anybody who sticks his nose in the door is hired. . . . New matrons have virtually no training. They are placed under observation of older matrons for one week, and then they're on their own."

The few male staff members hired by Westfield State Farm were called "patrolmen," and were not organized as in the male facilities with a military chain of command, from C.O., to sergeant, to lieutenant, to captain. A member of the maintenance crew was in charge of the patrolmen, and when he was away one of the painters took over.

Sadly enough the article went on to say that with all its problems, Westfield State Farm was one of the best women's prisons in the nation. "Others are much worse." Sister Elaine Roulet and other staff members who have occasion to visit other prisons today usually return with much the same report.

In the weeks that followed the lurid headlines, more media visitors came to Westfield and more articles were written. The issue of drugs coming into the prison prompted writers to criticize the prison's visiting process. "Inmate and visitors sit on opposite sides of a table, making it easy to pass contraband." However, a matron was present at all times and, by written instructions, was told, "Never leave a visitor alone with an inmate for even a fraction of a minute. When you leave the visiting room, take the inmate with you. If you are watching more than one girl, take both girls with you." Inmates at Bedford were referred to as "girls," or "our girls," and under one superintendent as "those poor devils," until 1970, when someone ordered that we be called "ladies." Today, it is the one rule that seems to have been carved deep into the brain of every C.O. They always call us "ladies," no matter what we're doing.

By the fall of 1958, the Commissioner of Corrections assured the press that conditions at Westfield State Farm had improved. The decision had been made to stop the farming program and concentrate on reading, writing and arithmetic, though some vestiges of the farming continued for several more years. When Reverend Baker, our Protestant minister here, arrived in 1960, what is now a large parking lot was a field of thriving corn. The eventual phasing out of small garden plots was, in my estimation, a giant step backward.

Last summer, having been removed from the honor cottage, I approached four levels of administration asking if I could please plant three small packets of seeds. The first one, a woman, was coy and cute and said, "Weeel, I'll have to think about it." I asked her three different times and as far as I know, though a new spring is here, she's still thinking about it. Several members of the church said it was fine if I planted around the chapel, but they couldn't give that kind of permission. We're talking heavy stuff now. A deputy superintendent said he'd have to ask someone else, too, but he'd get right back to me. That was nine months ago and he hasn't gotten back yet. A prison staff seems to attract and nourish people who are terrified of making the simplest decision. "This is the first I've heard of it," "I'll get back to you," are sounds most often heard. Common sense and the truth are the bogeymen of the system. It's an extremely poor atmosphere in which to teach anyone else to begin to grow up.

The fire hazards headlined by the press were not noticeably improved, and in my observation thirty years later they still haven't been, though a start has recently been made. The day in 1958 that a special fire inspection was held, the fire truck was locked in a garage and nobody could find the key. I have, this fall, seen a fire truck here, the first time in seven years. Two years ago, new fire exits were added to each end of the fifty-four-year-old medical building. When I asked a C.O. if there had been a fire drill yet to use the new exits, she shrugged, "Nobody's used 'em yet because nobody knows who's got the keys." I hope the paucity of well-organized drills and the presence of many untrained young officers who have a hard time trying to figure out how to open and close the cell doors will not go on until there is a terrible tragedy. The feeling of responsibility I had for youngsters in the schools where I taught and administered makes me very aware of this. Our drills were frequent, timed, and no one went back to classes until everyone was accounted for. In old buildings where careless women smoke day and night, the same rules should apply, and on a floor where twenty-nine babies live, they should apply doubly.

While the headlines hadn't mentioned poor food and too little food as playing a role in Westfield's poor morale, for the inmates it was the principal complaint. In June 1958, the girls, all dressed in their pink cotton uniforms, held a four-hour demonstration about it. Three days later, the demonstration erupted into a full-scale riot. Anna Kramer, who had just been named superintendent, announced a new "get tough" policy and assured anyone who was interested that there would be no more riots. And there weren't any more for almost fourteen years. Some of my friends and acquaintances were in the next one—were ringleaders, in fact.

Eleven

*For you will have missed the atmosphere of our House
unless you picture the whole place from week's end to
week's end buzzing, tittering, hinting, whispering, about
this subject.*

C. S. LEWIS

A woman's physical and emotional makeup have
been giving her a bad name ever since someone
started scratching pictures on cave walls, and even before. Woman has been the deviant since the Garden of
Eden. What is surprising is that so much of this attitude persists today. As Carol Gilligan observes in
Woman's Place in Man's Life Cycle, "We have been accustomed to seeing life through men's eyes." From female
as well as male C.O.s here you will hear that Sing
Sing is the norm and Bedford is the aberration, and
many of us accept that without wondering why.

The Greek word *hysterikos* translated literally means
"of the womb." The connection has plagued us ever
since. The field of gynecology, a discipline that came
into being in the nineteenth century, has always been
closely associated with pathology. The norms for human behavior are unquestionably established with

male behavior as the prototype. This has been especially true of criminal behavior even though female criminal behavior has certain distinctive characteristics. While only 5 percent of those incarcerated in the United States are women, the disciplinary problems of women, once there, are more intractable than those of men. The highest rates of offenses against prison discipline occur in female prisons, an estimated 300 offenses per 100 population of women, as against 150 offenses per 100 population of men. Self-mutilation is more common among women. Many times more psychotropic drugs are administered to women than to men. Psychiatric pathology among female inmates appears to be much more severe and extensive than pathology apparent in male inmates.

Crime and deviance are key social issues that have historically attracted many social theorists, but only from the standpoint of male criminals, rarely female. One of the few men to tackle the subject (until very recently) was Otto Pollak. In 1950, he wrote a book entitled, *The Criminality of Women,* in which he raked over many of the old coals Lombroso had lit and added some new ones. He wrote, "Women commit less crime than men because they have not evolved to the same degree as men, and are therefore more primitive, and have less scope for degeneration." Please note this is not a tract from the Middle Ages. I had graduated from college and my older son had been born by the time this appalling bit of information was let loose upon the reading public and its author was widely quoted through the 1970s.

Pollak kindly excused some of our criminality by observing, "For women, deviance . . . is a socially prescribed form of behavior." (I wonder if he ever married.) And while he seemed to blame female deviance on nature, at the same time he insisted it was pathological. In short, what is natural is unnatural. Women are wicked and saintly, mother and whore at the same

132

time. Obviously, he never did quite figure us out because he always measured us against male behavior, which is "normal."

Trying to follow Pollak's convoluted thinking on the subject of women explains in a small way the position of black women in the role of criminal. While black Americans live their lives around a culture of white norms, women have to live their lives around a culture of male norms as well, the result being that black women have the roughest time struggling with both norms in the search for their own identity. In her everyday life as well as in her treatment by the justice system, a black woman is unquestionably the most victimized of our citizens. She is seven times more likely to be raped than a white woman, or to be the victim of other violent crimes. She is imprisoned in greater proportion to her numbers than black men and all whites. She is more apt to be jailed for a victimless crime, and more apt to be returned to prison for a parole violation.

In one respect, Pollak was useful. He recognized the role of menstruation, pregnancy and menopause in exposing women to psychic trauma, weakening their inhibitions and creating a biological setting for crime.

The concept of menstrual and premenstrual tensions playing a role in female crime is a widely accepted belief today. "There is growing research showing that a majority of violent female crimes, like child abuse, assault, and murder take place just prior to or during menstruation." Some states have considered making the premenstrual syndrome a legitimate legal plea.

Pollak's sociology sprang from a kind of sexual politics. He reasoned that if a woman can fake an orgasm she can lie about anything. He scrambled culture and biology and came up with a soufflé called the female criminal. Unfortunately, he was one of so few writing about the female criminal in the 1950s that whether people agreed with him or not, he was widely quoted for the next twenty years. Few were interested enough in the subject to refute him. The paperback version of his book has a picture of a witch beating a kneeling man, which is about as scientific as much of Pollak's writing. Women, he repeated endlessly, are impelled by their physiology to be no damned good. On the other hand, he finally determined there is little connection between the biology of men and their crimes.

His thinking was not unlike that of the first Baron Baden-Powell, founder of the Boy Scouts, who is quoted as saying, "Scouting attracts the hooligans . . . who really are the fellows of character . . . well, the best class of boys." Can you imagine anyone saying of the Girl Scouts, "They attract the hooligans . . . the girls of character . . . well, the best class of girls." It is naive to suppose that this type of thinking is no longer with us. It is used to explain why prostitutes are punished but their customers are not. A woman who sells herself is behaving in an "unnatural way"; the "johns" are just being themselves. It's okay to punish whores because they're social outcasts anyway. Their customers, on the other hand, may be someone important and productive. The Mayflower Madam case is a monument to public hypocrisy.

Pollak predicted that the increasing emancipation of women would lead to more and more female crime. Was he right? Or is it coincidence? Or does it mean we are now evolving enough to be as degenerate as men?

Ms. Wyke, until recently head of the Medical Department here, last worked at Sing Sing. "Oh Jean," she said, "It's so much easier there than here." "Not for inmates," I said, "with all those terrible tiers of cells?" "Yes, for inmates and staff, too. Things are much more matter-of-fact there. Everyone accepts things better without constant arguing or tantrums. There's so much emotion here. It's exhausting." That's true.

It's like a constant humidity of 85 percent and just as enervating. Someone is always unhappy and letting others know it.

My own observation is that many of the women here fall loosely into two groups, the first made up of those so damaged in childhood they have never learned to trust and love or even feel small pangs of compassion for others; the second made up of those in whom the need to love and be loved is the overriding drive in their lives. And even those in the first group who are incapable of love reach out to others if only to use them instead of love them. For many the need to love was what brought them here and it often makes life miserable for them while they're here.

If she had a man or lover outside — someone who isn't already in prison as her codefendant — a woman can be pretty sure that he won't spend too much time visiting her or weeping over her imprisonment. There are a few faithful men who come, but two of these I suspect keep coming because *she* knows where the money is hidden.

The result is many women in prison develop a strong emotional attachment to another woman. Davis acknowledged that there were some homosexuals at the reformatory in 1908, but she never discussed them in her writings as a serious problem. Her policy was largely to ignore it or lecture the girls that it was "a naughty habit." Over the years, from what I have been able to read about the facility, homosexuality has been treated one of three ways: administration ignored it, administration denied that it existed, administration punished it when it was too overt to ignore or when the newspapers brought it to their attention. Mrs. Fish, superintendent in 1964, said in an interview, "There is very little homosexuality at Westfield. Strict disciplinary measures are enforced if there is evidence of it. . . . I insist that each girl have her own room."

The social and sexual revolutions of the 1960s and 1970s have changed all that. Overt homosexuality can be seen all around us. Sometimes strong relationships even grow between inmates and female C.O.s.

Some inmates when they leave even go to live with a C.O. It's done at great risk. If discovered the C.O. would lose his or her job and the parolee could be returned to prison as a parole violator (PV), so it doesn't happen often, but it does happen. Flora was so loved by one of the female C.O.s that she was permitted to lean against the officer's bubble for hours on end and visit with her, wearing only a filmy nightgown. It was that C.O. who asked me to write a letter to her landlord for her, requesting a move from a one-bedroom to a two-bedroom apartment. "When Flora comes out, I'm gonna need a room for my daughter."

I've watched many a woman wash, iron, and cook for her "butch," "dike," "bulldagger," and I've heard one stand outside a cell door, begging forgiveness for some wrongdoing she couldn't identify. "What did I do, Tony? I did it all just the way you told me. I can't do any more. How can you be mad at me, Tony?"

Her butch can be just as difficult as the man she left on the street, and just as inclined to have three or four other women on the string. This is socially acceptable because there are a lot more women than butches. If, however, the female has more than one "guy," she runs the risk of having the hell beat out of her by one or both of them. A prison is the home of social Darwinism. To the victors belong the spoils.

Many of the butches make a concentrated effort to emulate the behavior of young black males, the hip-walking, cool-talking model of masculinity. Some cut their hair short or shave their heads. They swagger when they walk, toes out, their arms positioned just so, near, but not touching their sides.

Some of the older ones are more dignified, still with short hair, man's shirt, V-neck sweater and men's

136

pointed-toed shoes. They are all muscular, strong, work out with weights in the gym and can often look more like men than women.

Sadly enough the inmates with beards and mustaches usually aren't the butches. The reason for this I don't know. Self-imposed tattoos are very popular here with lesbian and nonlesbian alike. They are made by scratching the letters or pictures with a pin or needle and then rubbing the area with India ink and cigarette ashes. I'm told "it sort of hurts." Obviously, they aren't meant as beauty spots. They're done out of boredom, out of a desire to be identified or to tell the world who their lover is or as a symbol of disrespect for their own bodies. Any or all of the above.

In 1972, the chief psychologist here wrote, "There's more homosexuality in women's prisons than in men's. Ninety-nine percent of the fights in Bedford Hills are two women fighting over a 'butch.' " I don't find that to be true. There are plenty of arguments about "butches" and women, but just as many over something else.

"Who took my cigarettes?" "Who took my fuckin' light bulb?" "Who put their wash in the dryer ahead of mine?" "Who changed the TV channel?" "Who took my gold chains?" These are also fought about and, of course, drugs. The two most vicious arguments in the facility in the past six months were about some stolen jewelry and the TV. The woman whose jewelry was stolen gathered together five of her thuggish friends, searched cells, and did vaginal and anal searches of some hapless women as well. Legally, this is known as sodomy and rape. The ringleader got four years in solitary, with lesser times for her friends. But they won an appeal and their time has since been reduced. The C.O. on the floor, who gave them plastic gloves for their search, as well as a sergeant who came on the floor while it was going on, still have their jobs. The jewelry was found in one of the big refrigerators in the kitchen.

The fight over the TV left a woman seriously injured. On the other hand, YaYa still has a bandage on her arm where her lover bit her in anger.

There is no one, anywhere, who can tell you exactly how prevalent homosexuality is, in prison or anywhere else. I read a nice, ladylike article in a local Connecticut paper in which the author ventured, "5 percent to 7 percent of women in prison are homosexuals. Even I guessed 25 percent. From an informal questioning of staff and inmates, over one hundred different people, I've had what was for me a surprising collection of answers to the question, "What percentage of the inmates do you think have a homosexual relationship while they are here?" Some went as high as 95 percent. When I suggested they were kidding, they suggested, "Lady, open your eyes." C.O.s and inmates gave similar answers. Answers differed in part depending upon whether the relationship was sexual or not. Most agree that the percentage of women who come in as lesbians and will go out to continue the same life is 20 percent to 25 percent. Those who are filling the need to be close to someone, to feel safe, to be told her hair looks nice, and sometimes, though not always, to replace the heterosexual sex she left behind, are estimated at between 65 percent and 85 percent.

One inmate said, "Hell. This is the theater district. They put on a big act, they'll flirt with anything that moves, but they're just heterosexuals puttin' on an act."

In the past seven years sexual mores in this prison seem to me to have changed noticeably. Perhaps it took me that long to see what I had always been looking at. The prison families which had been so much a part of women's prisons for many years are fewer now. One hears the call, "Mommy, Mommy," less frequently, except among the Puerto Ricans. They are the most family oriented here and stay close together.

It could, of course, be language, not family, that keeps them together. They also call old women like me, "Mommy," as a courtesy I think. It is true that one hears, "Hey Tony," "Hey Ricky," "Hey Stevie," "Hi Honey," and "I love ya, baby," more often than "Mommy." Perhaps the nuclear families of prison are disappearing with the nuclear families of the outside. It's more every woman for herself now, and it's tough.

Not all but many of the dikes support themselves by sweet-talking the women and providing a little sex. In return the ladies make sure she has cigarettes and a clean shirt. Inside, as well as outside, it's the woman who pays. Often the largest price she pays is in guilt, a guilt she may carry with her after she goes back to a man. Perhaps when we've made feminists of them all, the guilt will fade.

Some of the women seem genuinely confused as to where their preferences lie. Benjie gets all dolled up when "Ma man" is coming. Then three days later she wipes off the lipstick assumes the male walk and mannerisms and starts calling out the window to "Ma honey-cake." Her need for affection is palpable. She has a "mommy and a daddy" in here, too. They are an accepted lesbian couple and they befriend her from time to time. While making lunch one Saturday morning, they made a sandwich for Benjie, too, and put it in her cell for her. When she discovered it, she cried out in childish delight, "I've got the best mommy and daddy in the whole world." When her wants are not quickly met she can become as obscene and violent as she is cute and cuddly when she is moved to be.

Sex in general, sex in particular, is the primary subject of interest in here, for the C.O.s as well as the inmates. I know a C.O. who impregnated both an inmate and another C.O. in a short space of time while he was married to yet another. He was found out, suspended for six months and told he was a naughty boy.

It is not unusual for female C.O.s as well as inmates to be unmarried mothers and to have a different man for each child.

A fairly popular ceremony in here is the marriage of two women, often complete with a little veil, a few wild flowers, a friend to serve as minister and another to serve as witness. The corner of the yard is the usual spot for the ceremony. When the weather is cold, or when a C.O. doesn't care what goes on during his tour of duty, the rites are performed in someone's cell. Why do they do this? A study commissioned under the Reagan administration noted that in 1960 there were seventy employed black men ages twenty to twenty-four for every one hundred black women the same age. Today there are fifty employed, marriagable black men for every one hundred black women in the same age group. This also speaks to the number of single-parent families.

But male shortages are not the only reason that women seek out another woman for friend and lover and black women are certainly not the only ones concerned. Many couples here are racially mixed. More than half the women in here have been sexually abused at one time in their lives, some as small children by father, uncle, granddad, mother's lover. They fear men, even despise men. There are hookers who hate men. There are some very young girls in here who are afraid to function in prison without a "protector." But perhaps the best explanation for the sexual behavior in here came from Evelyn. Explaining her relationship with another woman one week and her passionate visit with a man in the visiting room the next week, she shrugged, "A girl's gotta do what a girl's gotta do."

Until recently lovers in this prison were, for the most part, assigned to different cell blocks and kept away from one another as much as possible. The ingenuity with which (rules notwithstanding) they can still

140

reach one another, on stairwells, in the gym, the chapel, the library and many other places, too, is formidable, if not praiseworthy. A few twosomes are permitted to live side by side, and have for years. They manage to live without serious lover's quarrels, which may be why they aren't separated.

But now a new program is being instituted here, probably unique to this facility — lovers are permitted to live near one another, if they come forward and ask the superintendent for the privilege. They must believe their relationship will be long-standing and peaceful and agree to visit a psychiatrist together on a regular basis. Whether this will accomplish anything useful, or prove a very bad idea, remains to be seen. The psychiatrists' point of view about lesbianism is certainly one of the key ingredients. Will they bless the unions or try to talk the women out of them? I am told, to date, they are nonjudgmental and helpful. What will probably do the program in will be what did in school prayer and the pledge of allegiance. The nonlesbians will start demanding equal time and demand to live next to their best friends, too. Either that, or there'll be so many lovers' quarrels it won't work. I've already seen the lady member of one of the twosomes sporting a black eye. But it was a quiet fight and she still looks happy.

C. S. Lewis, in his splendid autobiography of his early school years entitled *Surprised by Joy,* says of the prevalence of homosexuality in a boys' boarding school and later in college, "I suppose it might be called 'The Greek Tradition.' But the vice in question is one to which I had never been tempted, and which indeed I find opaque to the imagination. . . . As things were, I was bored."

The line between innocence and ignorance may sometimes be so finely drawn that one can be mistaken for the other. Yet one is a gift and one a curse. I cannot say as Lewis did that the subject has ever bored me. For most of my life the subject simply didn't exist for me. Today, what awareness I have of it saddens me a little, leaves me feeling something is amiss that I will never understand or that there is a loneliness and emptiness so deep in the lives of some of these women that they will grasp at anything to fill the void and make the hurting go away. I'm sure there are those who will interpret that as ignorance, too, which it may well be. Like Lewis, I can only say, "I will not indulge in futile philippics against enemies I have never met in battle."

As I write this, I am haunted by thoughts of Pam and Pritzie. Pritzie's constant search for a friend, someone she could shower with attention and receive the same in return, though not quite typical is not unique in here. "I love ya, Pammy," she would call across the hall. "Ya know what I'm gonna do today . . . ? Oh, you gonna like it. I'm gonna make ya laugh. We gonna have such a good time. So get you all dressed up and we gonna go down to the rec. Put on somethin' nice now . . . I'm gettin' all dressed up. You gonna love the way I look."

In time Pam "maxed out," that is, she served her maximum sentence and was let go. Five days later her body was found, horribly mutilated, on the roof of an empty building. Pritzie cried when she found out but the crying soon stopped. She's a poor neighbor, Pritzie, because she is never quiet. Most of the time she is just talking to herself. I heard her one morning shortly after Pam's death. "Pammy's dead. She went and died on me . . . It ain't my fault . . . That's all right . . . Everything's gonna be all right . . . I don't need nobody . . . long's my mother send me fifty dollars." Pritzie lives her life between losses. I think she's a little crazy, which under the circumstances is probably the most rational response. Or maybe she isn't crazy. Maybe her problem is she just isn't a man.

It is perhaps a strange postscript to tell you there

are a few true love affairs spawned in here, between the locked Capulet and Montagu, the keeper of the keys, young love complete with starry eyes and longing and respect. It is of course destined to die of starvation somewhere in the endless labyrinth of bureaucracy. But you must believe that with all the ugliness there are some true innocents in here, young people surprisingly pure and unsullied, some you would gladly claim for your own. Even with love unrequited, they are the lucky ones.

Twelve

The courts have done more to improve conditions in our nation's prisons and jails than any other individual organization or branch of government.

NORMAN CARLSON
FORMER DIRECTOR, U.S. BUREAU OF PRISONS

"Reduce Crime by Care of Young," cried a *New York Times* headline of April 1923. "For Children: A Fair Chance, Stop Wasting Lives and Money," said a *New York Times* article dated September 1987.

The 1923 article, specifically about Bedford, went on to say, "The group of women here studied is characterized by a high degree of physical defectiveness, defects that are preventable in that they are the result of family nutrition, bad hygiene, bacterial infections, and other concomitants of unintelligence and poverty."

The August 1987 issue of *Corrections Magazine,* trade magazine of the American Corrections Association, is devoted to articles about handicapped prisoners. It notes, "There is an overpopulation of handicapped men and women in our jails and prisons, and a study conducted by Maryland's Division of Corrections shows that handicapped inmates spend more time in segrega-

144

tion, where they get virtually no adequate treatment or educational services." It specifies "handicapped" as those with physical disabilities, health impaired, the mentally retarded, emotionally disturbed, or those having specific learning disabilities. It adds that such handicapped inmates have two and a half times as many disciplinary infractions as the nonhandicapped and three times as many days in solitary. As I write this, there are five women on my floor "in lock" for misbehavior. Each one is seriously emotionally disturbed.

Dr. Edith Spaulding wrote in 1923, "Our greatest need is for better trained staff who understand these women, and can help them."

Corrections Magazine, August 1987, claims, "C.O.s today have little or no training in how to handle the handicapped, that is, those who are not fully aware of the consequence of their behavior."

Sixty-five years span the distance between those observations and little has happened to improve things. If anything the problem has grown worse. In 1986 the keynote speaker at the 116th Congress of the American Correction Society said, in the opening paragraph of his speech, "multiple issues continue to plague Corrections — psychosis, alcohol and drugs, violence, sex offenders, cultural and racial issues, language barriers, selfishness and irresponsibility, developmental disabilities, mixed loyalties, treatment needs and myths, training needs, affirmative action, contraband, stress, inadequate funding, dishonesty, legal actions and liabilities, *and these are only some of the staff problems.* A similar though longer list could be made of offender problems!" Not much longer! Who was it that asked, "And who will guard the guardians?"

In February 1963, President John F. Kennedy gave an address to Congress in which he recommended a community health program for the entire country, to take mental patients out of large, impersonal state institutions and put them instead into small community homes. New York's Governor Nelson Rockefeller thought it was a good idea, which it was, but only half of the idea was carried out. Many thousands of patients were released from mental institutions, but communities didn't want them; in fact, fought hard to keep them out. Nobody wants criminals or "crazies" in their neighborhood. "It brings down the value of real estate."

In all candor, as I think about it, if someone had suggested a home for paroled women, a drug detox station or a home for the mentally impaired in my neighborhood in Grosse Pointe Farms, I would have resisted it, too. Ignorance and our national fanaticism about money play a large role in our civic behavior. The average citizen, like many who go to prison, do what they do because they are isolated and don't know, or prefer not to consider, the long-term effects of their behavior. In 1965 there were more than eighty-five thousand patients in New York mental hospitals. Today, there are fewer than twenty thousand.

While the census of mental hospitals declined, prison populations exploded. How much was cause and effect and how much was happenstance is hard to say. By and large, mental hospitals took only the profoundly retarded or psychotic, while prisons usually hold the moderately impaired—usually but not always.

Many of the programs meant to care for the mentally ill at Bedford today are less than fifteen years old. In 1977 the responsibility for providing prison mental health care passed from the Department of Corrections (DOC), to the Office of Mental Health (OMH). Prior to that, the two largest facilities in New York State for psychiatric patients were Dannemora and Matteawan state hospitals. By 1976, both were "phased out" as hospitals and are now prisons for men. A former prison neighbor of mine spent six years as a young woman at Matteawan. As an aging woman she is now in prison, a constant source of misery and mayhem for herself and everyone around her. There has to be some place for her—and prison is now it.

Separation of OMH and DOC was a good idea in some respects, especially since the numbers of criminals and mentally ill keep growing. Unfortunately, as can happen between departments in large companies, the exchange of information between the two does not always flow evenly or constantly. For-me-to-know-and-you-to-find-out is a game played by adults as well as children. DOC may permit a woman into regular population without knowing about her former treatment by OMH. Records are only as valuable as their availability and use.

OMH does not evaluate the mental problems of each woman who comes to Bedford. If they have a known record of mental problems or arrive behaving in an overtly dangerous manner, they are referred to the mental health department. Otherwise they go through the regular orientation and test program.

Every woman sentenced to prison in New York State now comes first to Bedford Hills for orientation and classification. Theoretically all are given the group IQ, the revised Beta, in English and Spanish. I don't remember taking it, but maybe I did. Every woman who tests 70 or below on the group IQ is then administered an individual test, the Wechsler Adult Intelligence Scale Revised, which does not require reading or writing. That is, they are given this test when a qualified test administrator is available, which is not all the time. Giving the test is close to a full-time job here. The only person qualified to give it is also a full-time teacher. At hearings in 1920 about treatment of inmates, the superintendent testified that each inmate was going to be thoroughly tested for classification purposes as soon as a certain staff member had caught up with her other work. The staff member then testified she wasn't qualified to do the testing.

If a woman has a diagnosable mental disorder, a history of mental health treatment or is withdrawn and depressed and obviously lacking in social and self-care skills, she is first placed in the Intermediate Care Program (ICP) which was introduced to Bedford in 1980, and where it is hoped she can be worked gradually into the regular prison population. It is, in a small way, an attempt to go back to what Davis tried to do eighty years ago. The largest difference between the treatment of these women and all the others here is that they, for the most part, are not classified into prison jobs or programs. They have group meetings, arts and crafts, games and some academic tutoring. Their cells are a little smaller than regular ones, and their bath and shower room is a disgrace, if not a certifiable health hazard. While sports were originally intended to be an important part of the ICP program, they play little or no part today. The women are largely sedentary and must be coaxed outside merely to observe a sporting event, let alone take part in one.

While the original intent was that ICP was to be a temporary detour on the way to the regular prison population, it hasn't worked out that way for many. More and more women are serving their entire sentences in some area of the mental health department, or are moved only toward the end of their stay to qualify for parole. A report by Diane Steelman, published by the Correctional Association of New York in January 1987, estimates that 10 percent to 12 percent of women entering Bedford need ICP housing. The unit can handle 28 women, 70 is 10 percent. My own opinion from six years of observation is that 125 women would be a more reasonable estimate. Bedford has repeatedly asked for funding to enlarge ICP but so far hasn't received it.

Women sentenced to three years or less, or having only three years left on a longer sentence, are sent from Bedford to Albion, a medium-security prison outside of Buffalo. However, since Albion lacks facilities to handle mental cases, those women, however long or short their terms, remain here. The obvious result is that the number of psychotics at Bedford grows larger and larger. They settle to the bottom, like silt, and stay here. The difference this has made here in the past seven years can be seen and heard. When I ask staff members who have served here for more than five years, "Do you see a difference in the women here today?" I get the same answer. "Anger, there is more anger here now."

If a woman in ICP "goes off," which means shrieks and screams, attacks someone, throws and breaks things or tries suicide by carving her name into her arm or swallowing a bed spring (it has been done), she is moved to another part of the alphabet, PSU, Psychiatric Satellite Unit, where there is a small dormitory with six beds and three observation cells with nothing but a mattress on the floor. Into one of these cells a woman is placed, stark naked so there is nothing with which to hurt herself. While this may sound cruel, it is not done out of sadism. Apparently there comes a point at which, short of handcuffs or straitjackets, there seems little else to do until the woman quiets down. One small hitch is that they are supposed to be observation cells and one has to get down on hands and knees to look in. I am told this area is soon to be enlarged.

If Satellite cannot help the woman, she is handcuffed, chained and driven the six-hour trip to Central New York Psychiatric Center at Marcy. I have seen a woman thus chained, so strong that three large men had trouble getting her into the backseat of a car. Stays at Marcy can be six or more weeks long — or forty-eight hours. There is one sad woman who has made countless trips to Marcy only to be judged "fine" and returned within forty-eight hours. Saddest of all, she is an intelligent and articulate woman; even when shouting and screaming and threatening, she often makes good sense. There are some people nobody knows what to do with, and she is one of them. I think in time some are let out because everyone is exhausted. When one sees some of the women paroled there is no other conclusion to reach.

Many women I know who have been to Marcy, speak highly of it. Some want to go back. "It's coed, Jean, and the food is better and there's lots of things to do, and a pool table." While there is room there for over two hundred prisoners, they are, we're told, treated as patients, not inmates. That and a more structured environment must give them the feeling of security one doesn't have here. But then we can't go to the other extreme and empty the prisons into mental hospitals.

At Bedford, and other prisons as well, the final stop in the mental health department, if not Marcy, is solitary confinement — SHU, Segregation Housing Unit. The women who use their energy howling, throwing urine or feces on anyone who walks by, start fires, or generally trash their cells, are sent, for long periods of time, to solitary. When the confinement drives them almost out of their minds, they are taken to Marcy for treatment. When they return somewhat chastened — if not by treatment, by drugs — they are locked right back in solitary to experience again the treatment that sent them to Marcy.

This letter came to a friend of mine from a woman in SHU:

CARMEN I NEED TOOTHPASTE
I Need my shit to do what I have to do things will look up if we stick together for that is how the almighty Gods see it also need my familys pictures I love them with all my Heart and Soul. MY Mother always looks out for me for I am her only daughter and I will Someday have my own for this is my purpose in Life the Almighty Gods say I must bare a child another God or Goddess will be born But I choose my own Man on the street Love But if I get a siezier and die what is the Medical

Department gonna say How are they gonna explain that I also need to see my family But if they can't make it up here for some reason I'll guess I have to understand for I don't want to *Hurt* her in any way for I love my family and anyone who hurts my family will now that the Gods in heaven don't lie for the Gods always wine But don't play. there are a lot of officers here who are full of shit all they want is time off. I hav done all that I have to do But I need Everyones cooperation in order to go on for I am Human and like all Humans we all have needs and needs will always over rule wants. I want to go home But I need to see my family because it makes me feel Good when I see people that I know really and truly love me God watches all my enemies and Believe me nothing can hurt me for I am a true Believer.
right now I'm feeling very weak and I feel like throwing up My Right hand hurts and
  just remember I worked in Midtown South OK and my PO is Mr. Blum I love him and the Guardian angels ride the trains

Love and peace always

One of these days, soon or late, the writer will be handed $40, a coat and a dress, and told to go and make her way among the good people. What would you say her chances are?

Putting seriously mentally ill inmates into solitary confinement is a chronic problem in all of our prisons, though I am most familiar with practice in New York. In a case brought in behalf of Attica inmates, in February 1988, a federal judge determined that solitary "is clearly not conducive to the development of a patient-therapist relationship whereby the inmate may receive meaningful treatment." His order bars the prison officials at Attica from placing or maintaining inmates

151

with severe mental disorders in the disciplinary section of the unit. It also requires that when an inmate's clothes are taken from him for more than fifteen minutes he be given paper clothing or a blanket. The lawsuit was prompted by the case of an Attica inmate with a record of mental illness who hanged himself. He had not had a single visit by a psychiatrist for two months prior to his suicide. The prison psychiatrist stated that inmates as a group are manipulative and therefore not deserving of credibility. The judge termed the statement "reprehensible." Unfortunately his decision affects only Attica. Apparently progress must be made on a prison by prison basis and there are fifty state prisons in New York.

Certainly prisoners are manipulative, and the mental cases are particularly so. It seems to me that is one of the symptoms of their illnesses. Awareness of this, one would hope, is lesson one for a prison psychiatrist. Unfortunately it doesn't seem to be lesson anything for C.O.s. I watch some of the women jerk C.O.s around like puppets on a string. There is a woman currently on my corridor in lock for a month. There are three young, white males on duty from 7:00 A.M. to 3:00 P.M. She calls for their services by yelling, "One a you dumb motherfuckin' honkie assholes—" One always comes running to provide what she demands. "I'm the king," she yells. "We doin' it my way." She is to be paroled in two months. The outside world is not waiting for her and nothing has been done to apprise her of this. She is simply endured until she can be gotten rid of. It is cruel for her and those who must endure her and even for those who inevitably will refuse to endure her outside. She is a walking time bomb.

A lawsuit, not unlike the Attica one, was recently brought against Thomas Coughlin, Commissioner of New York Department of Corrections, concerning mental health care at Bedford Hills Correctional Facility. The judgment requires the defendants to increase

152

the mental health care available to women in SHU (Segregated Housing Unit), "including an initial mental health evaluation with any appropriate treatment and placement recommendations; to make changes in the keeping of mental health files; and to train certain facility personnel in mental health issues." It also requires that a psychiatrist not employed by the state monitor the delivery of mental health care at the facility for at least the next two years. A doctor in Fort Lauderdale, Florida, was chosen to do the monitoring. Mine is not to reason why.

The case was brought in the first place because the solitary confinement building has long been used as a place to keep the most unruly mental cases, with the result that many grew more seriously pathological while there. Moreover, if they were removed from SHU to go to Marcy when they are returned to Bedford, they are made to finish their terms in SHU, often ending up in need of a trip to Marcy again. Whether that practice will now cease I don't know. The fact is the prisons have been put in a position where that's about all they can do if they are to be made to serve as both prisons and hospitals for the chronically mentally ill.

One soon discovers here the irony of the American public's fear that some criminals will plead insanity and "get away with murder." There are far more prisoners who probably should have pled insanity and didn't who should be getting a kind of psychiatric care they will never get, and who will serve their prison terms, many of them, and be back on the street to cause more tragedies for others and for themselves. Our compulsive need for retribution instead of understanding does us in far more than we know or care to hear about. The 1980s I'm afraid will be remembered by historians, perhaps even archaeologists, as "The Age of the Prison Builders."

Thirteen

"I done it 'cause I felt in dat mood in dat minute."

Three of us have played bingo once a week with the women in ICP for five and a half years and have grown to know some of them well. The purpose of the game originally was to bring a little amusement into their lives and at the same time to provide prizes of cigarettes, candy, soaps and other toiletries that aren't provided by the state and many can't afford to buy. But Sheila, Carmen and I who go together, enjoy it too and look forward to going. The women are always ready with their bingo cards waiting expectantly. I find many of them just as congenial and easy to get along with as the women anywhere else in the facility. But then they like the bingo, and work at behaving. They can't practice self-control indefinitely, so from time to time they disappear into Satellite or Marcy and then come back again. Some graduate into "regular population" which isn't much better. Some are sick enough to be satisfied with their lot. Dorothy rocks back and forth, tongue hanging out and tells you in a disinterested way that she has seven children. "Who's taking care of them, Dorothy?" I ask. She thinks for a moment, "My mother's got 'em." "That's a very big job for her, Dorothy." "It ain't so big. I had

154

'em," she says and goes happily back to her card game.

Many others are aware of their lot and live in a mental straitjacket that leaves them frantic and frustrated, ready to punish the world for their discomfort. With the exception of prescribed drugs to calm them, drugs that became available in the 1960s, we do little or nothing to help them. And the drugs, useful as they may be, have not proved the panacea that was originally hoped. Getting the right pills in the right quantities can take a long time in here, leaving the woman a mental and physical yoyo in the process. Sometimes a woman simply refuses to take any more medicine, and she can't be forced to.

We are told delinquent psychopaths can be helped today with special therapy, but the amount of therapy required makes it prohibitively expensive. It is unrealistic to suppose it will ever be used on inmates. Some are paroled to mental hospitals, but many just land back on the street.

One of my bingo friends who was recently paroled to Pilgrim State Hospital, a mental hospital, has apparently lucked out and found a spot where she is happy. She sounds a little lonely though. She wrote me last week, (or rather, had one of the aides write me) to say she thinks I would be happier there than here. She described some of the programs that one can "work up to" and where one can even have a key to her own room. Included in the letter, which I can only interpret as a genuine kindness on her part, is the name of the head of the hospital whom she suggests I write in order to make the move. I think she's just lonely for a friendly and familiar face.

The emptiness, the lack of warmth and compassion in the lives of many women here are the same stories Dr. Edith Spaulding and Katherine Davis studied and wrote about eighty years ago. They are hard to describe, hard for you and me to relate to. Candy brought it home to me last Saturday night. We had finished the bingo game and broken up into four tables for the game of

Spades. Candy, who is here for twenty to life for pushing a stranger in front of an oncoming subway train, was sitting beside me watching us play. Suddenly, she said, "I knew a old lady like you once. I carried her groceries for her. She gimme a dime. She was nice." What happens to a human being between the time she carries an old lady's groceries and pushes a stranger in front of a subway train?

The woman Candy pushed was pushed three days after Candy had been released with a clean bill of health from an overcrowded mental ward. "She's fine." I've never seen her be fine. "God," the C.O. in ICP said, "think what a relief this is to her family. They can sleep with both eyes closed now." It isn't much of a relief to her victim or to her. She's jumpy and pushy and nasty. She's quick to threaten and frightened when someone calls her bluff. The first bingo night she was here, she couldn't sit long enough or concentrate long enough to play. She spent the evening stalking another woman who couldn't sit still either. They pursued one another slowly, stealthily around the fringes of the room, arms stiff against the wall, legs apart and bent as though ready to spring. Five steps, by one of them, sliding along the wall—then a leap by the second, then more steps by the first. They were like nothing so much as jungle animals. The bingo game went on for over an hour, while they leapt and crept and paused and listened again. By the time they finally stopped, I could feel my pulse racing. The other women seemed not to notice. The C.O.s watched, fascinated, ready to step in, waiting for one or the other to be "caught."

Candy and so many other women like her are with no social skills at all, totally unconcerned about cause and effect, without compassion or concern for anyone, egocentric in the extreme. But behavior in ICP is not much different than behavior on my floor. A woman may amuse herself at midnight as Sally has, yelling someone's name at the top of her lungs—"Coco," "Hey Coco,"

156

"Fuck it! Coco, I'm callin' ya." This may be repeated eight or nine times before Coco finally wakes up and says sleepily, "Yeah." "Hey Coco, you got my Spiegel catalogue?" "Yeah." "Well stick it under the door so's the C.O. can bring it to me." She then starts yelling for the C.O. by name, the tone of her voice the same as one might use on an errant dog. The C.O. then has the choice of going like a good dog and retrieving the Spiegel catalogue or letting the woman scream for what may turn into two hours of chaos. I have heard this and similar scenes acted out a hundred times, and *never,* not once have I heard anyone angry with the inmate. The C.O. soon becomes the target of catcalls and obscenities. "Give her the fuckin' catalogue." The antisocial behavior of such women is endured and encouraged, leaving the woman all the more unable to adjust when she leaves here, which she will inevitably do. I have heard a woman yell out her sexual preferences from 10:00 P.M. lock-in to 1:20 A.M., by the clock, in a manner that went beyond obscene to primitive. No one, not an inmate, not four officers said one word to her. And not Jean Harris, either. I sat in my cell, knowing I would end up with a charge sheet for starting a riot if I opened my mouth, hating all of us for our cowardice more than the psychopath who was the instrument for our cowardice. The grim tragedy of much of this behavior at Bedford today is that it is treated as though it were normal acceptable behavior. At least sixty years ago, there was some attempt to improve behavior instead of a conscious effort to ignore it.

"He keep tellin' me calm down. You can't keep people from bein' upset. He ain't God. He ain't no motherfuckin' miracle worker. I ain't taken no more medicine. He can't make me take it. I'll throw it up. I got to deal with it within myself. He better get off my back cause that ain't gonna help none. That gonna make me have more seizures. Dumb ass motherfuckin' hillbilly — sad-assed motherfucker. I hope your mother drops dead. He gotta nerve ridin' shotgun on me and he ain't got no motherfuckin' sense."

Sometimes a woman's behavior reflects a kind of childish egotism beyond which she has never developed. LaVerne stands in front of the mirror in her cell and practices a rap song endlessly — endlessly. She has practiced the same song for eight months. In between verses she puts on another four coats of fingernail polish. White with black dots, black with red dots, stripes in pink, blue and green. By the time she has served her sentence, she will, if the past eight months are an accurate level of measurement, have put on over five thousand coats of nail polish. It will be her main accomplishment for seven years of her life — and it will be permitted because prison is a home for the idle, the unambitious and the just plain sick.

Her excuses for not going to work are varied: she havin' her period; she about to have her period; she just done had her period; it's rainin'; it's snowin'; it's too hot and it's too cold; she just don't feel like it; or "nobody woke me." For good or for ill the whim of the moment rules. A woman who arrived two hours late to a meeting with Sister Elaine explained, "Well I was up late last night writin' a letter to my grandmother." Shanequa not only refused to go to work one day, she was ready to fight for the privilege. "You know what that motherfucker tell me to do? Empty the garbage. On my birthday! I don't work on my birthday. Who the shit he think he is?" I wish I could say that any serious efforts are made here to retrain those attitudes, but the simple truth is they aren't. Sheila and I finally girded our loins and told the students in the Parenting Through Films class that the class starts at 3:30 and no one can enter after 3:45. This met with the usual "Who the fuck she think she is? She got a number just like me," but we've stuck to the rule.

Others have the same kind of exaggerated vanity that keeps them fixing their hair and grooming one another ad nauseum; an exaggerated sense of self which makes them constantly self-pitying and self-justifying. They have elevated the blaming of others to an art. Whatever happens to them is someone else's fault. Three times in my six and a half years here, I have, in moments of great weakness, asked a woman to make less noise. The first time I ended up with a charge sheet for "inciting a riot." The second time ended in a tie. The third time was when I asked Georgine to please sing a little softer. She puts her Walkman on and sings to it. Unfortunately, she is tone deaf and the closest thing I have heard to the sounds she makes were those of a taxi driver in New York who entertained me with sounds he assured me were "from very old Chinese opera." At any rate, after enduring several hours of it, I asked Georgine to sing quieter. The diatribe that followed, and went on another hour at least, will remain fresh enough in my mind, I hope, so that I will not make the same mistake a fourth time. "Oh ma Gawd!" she exploded. "Now I ain't happy no more. I was happy singin' ma little song, just singin' ma little song, I was happy. But that old bitch don't want me to be happy. She don't want no one to be happy. She just wanna see me be unhappy. Just singin' a little song." Adelaide, who had only moments before stopped by to borrow cigarettes we both know she will never return, quickly joined the fun, yelling out among other things that just because I lend her cigarettes, "don't mean you can go around makin' people unhappy." Actually, she and Georgine cordially loathe one another. It was not a case of one woman supporting another one, just two very sick women shouting into the wind.

Sometimes bizarre behavior, or what may seem bizarre to me, is simply a reflection of religious custom. "Matilda she faithful to Chang. The motherfuckin' gods tell her to jump out the window, she jump." Matilda puts pennies at her door and window, risking a charge sheet since any amount of money in prison is contraband, in order to insure her safety. The charge sheet is a small thing compared to the evil spirits that could slip into her cell when the pennies aren't there. Pennies and water keep her safe. Jars, cans, cups — a bucket, if she can find one — filled with water, stand in every free space in her cell. Sometimes they spill and flow out into the corridor and under other cell doors. A friend usually mops up the mess without saying a word. It isn't unusual for the women to shriek obscenities and insults over a tea bag or a comb. But they never scream at Matilda's occasional floods. There seems to be a tacit understanding that we each survive the best way we can and Matilda's survival requires pennies and water. Furthermore, they don't play fast and lose with anyone's religion, with the exception of Jews, whom they seem to have little use for. "Religions is all the same. They's one God, only one God. They just divide It up in parts. Except for them Jews. They the ones fucked it all up."

While many of the women profess to be Catholic, it's their own version of Catholicism, with undertones of religions that came with their ancestors from West Africa. Belief in magic and powerful spirits spread from Africa to the West Indies and parts of our South. Diane tells me, "I hadda Aunt put roots on me and my mother tell me 'Stop,' you ain't comin' in my house till the roots is gone. She fill a big tub with water, thrown in some plants and shit and make me climb in before I go back in the house."

Belief that one can put "roots" on another and wish them harm is believed by many of the women here. When their hair is cut they're careful about its disposal. They will let only a trusted friend have a picture of their children: Such things can be used to represent the person one wants to harm. An inmate who was here in the medical building in a wheelchair when I first arrived made a prison living for herself playing on the superstitions of others. She came in, ill and indigent, with no family to bring her anything. Somehow she convinced a few women that with her special powers she could "put roots on people" and make terrible things happen to

160

them. "Bring me a snip of their hair or fingernail clippings and I'll do the rest," she promised them. Since a prison is full of people who want to get even with someone else, she soon had a thriving business going, and her fame spread to all parts of the prison. She was called "the Witch of Bedford," and for a year or two every mishap in the facility — a broken finger, a failing grade on the GED exam, parole not granted — was credited by someone to the Witch of Bedford, a reputation she worked hard to foster.

Obviously, this kind of talent wasn't offered gratis. The price was cigarettes, the number determined by the amount of damage requested. Father Gorman tells me when the woman died she had a lifetime supply of cigarettes squirreled away in boxes and bags.

Fourteen

The supreme happiness of life is the conviction we are loved.

VICTOR HUGO

"I'm just as good as you are" is the cry of each of us. When you stop believing it, survival becomes very difficult. And it's true. In the eyes of God I feel comfortably sure we're all equal. But not in the American job market. Not in the buyers' and sellers' market in this country. And not when we infringe upon each other's culture without adapting to some of the requirements of that culture—simply crying "black is beautiful" isn't enough. I wonder if the person who gave us that slogan did it out of love for his fellow black person or as a sop to throw. It hasn't done much for the women in here. It makes the chip on the shoulder a little broader, but it doesn't convince them. It doesn't make them like themselves any more. It only broadens the distance between them and the people who don't need to be told "black is beautiful," who like what's inside, who like what they've accomplished whatever their color.

Deciding whose behavior is or is not abnormal, and why, is an imprecise skill at best. Culture may, and often does, determine the answer. Each society has its set of rules or norms for "right" or "wrong," and those rules are absorbed in childhood. Dr. Matsuzaka, a psychiatrist formerly here at the prison whom I visited every two or three weeks and who was a very important source of comfort and strength to me over these prison years, thinks there is less psychopathology in the prison than others estimate. He believes that culture—the ways of life learned at home and in the neighborhood—bears more of the responsibility for the behavior in here than true pathology. This may well be true, but if the final result mimics pathology, it still should be treated and changed in order for each individual to be accepted back into the prevalent society.

I don't begin to know all the reasons our minds fail us and our behavior becomes bizarre or unattractive or dangerous. I know my memory of Bedford's social misfits will always be first of those women who are only asking for attention, calling out any way they can, "Look at me. Look at me. I'm a woman. I'm a person. I matter. Look at me."

Connie is one of these. We are locked in our cells and counted four times a day, at 6:30 A.M., 12:30 P.M., 5:30 P.M. and 10:00 P.M. At these times, privacy curtains must be down so each of us can be easily and quickly seen. At least twice a day, usually in late afternoon and evening, Connie leaves her curtain up. This way the C.O. has to stop his count at her door and ask her to take her curtain down. Her answer is always the same, "I'm on the toilet." His answer is always the same, "Lady, I gotta see ya. Put out your hand or somethin'." Connie argues and complains and finally sticks out a hand or tells him to come back. At 10:00 P.M., when we are locked in for the night, she waits fifteen minutes or so, and then calls, "Officer, officer. I need a match." Or a cigarette or another light bulb, or a magazine or whatever. "I left it in the rec. Get it for me." She has to have

163

special attention.

Several weeks ago she'd had a particularly poor day. Even when she isn't calling for attention, she gets it by talking to herself loud enough for others to hear. "Oh, Jesus, my Savior, I gotta get outta here. These bitches drivin' me crazy. Look at this place. Fuckin' mess. Gotta get me outta this crazy place." About half of the women on the floor were locked in for the night. Some had gotten a "late night," that is permission to watch a special movie until 11:00 P.M. Connie and I were locked in. Quiet for ten minutes and then a rap on the wall between our cells. "Jean. You gotta rope?" "A rope? How would I have a rope? It's contraband, I think." Silence for about ten more minutes and then a rap on the wall and, "Jean. You gotta razor?" I had one. Safety razors are allowed, but I wasn't about to give it to someone who had just asked for a rope. "Sorry, Connie. I don't." There was quiet for about fifteen more minutes, then an urgent banging on the wall. "Jean, call the C.O. Call the C.O."

I started to call in my little soprano falsetto, "C.O. Officer. Officer. Connie needs you. Please come." Finally another woman heard me and roused the C.O. He opened Connie's cell door and rushed to her doorway. "What's the matter? What's the matter?" he asked.

"Nothing's the matter," she announced airily. "I just asked Harris for a rope so I could hang a shelf and a razor because I wanted to shave under my arms, and she got all excited and thought I was trying to kill myself." Several women heard the commotion now and came down the hall. They stopped outside my cell while Connie explained, "It's nothing. Just Harris got all excited because she thought I was gonna kill myself." It was a splendid joke to end the day with. There were three of them now and Connie standing outside my locked door, laughing, shrieking, cackling, not women anymore but witches stirring their caldron with me in the middle of it.

I sat on my bed, hugging my knees, pretending I was calm, trying to remember what sanity was like.

The next morning Connie came to my open door and started to speak. "Connie," I said, "Go away and don't come back. What you did last night was not only dangerous, it was unspeakable. If you ever want to put on a performance like that again, don't ring my bell, because I'll just roll over and go back to sleep."

"Well I was mad at you because you told the C.O." "Come off it, Connie. I did exactly what you wanted me to. Why didn't you call the C.O. yourself? You have a voice that breaks glass—but instead you asked me to call. It was a rotten thing to do. Now go away."

For two weeks Connie seemed chastened—her voice was rarely heard. Finally, one afternoon, she came to my door again. "Jean." "Yes?" "Have you noticed how good I been?" "Yes, Connie. You've been fine." "You know why I've been so good?" "No." "Because I want you to be my friend again." She's fifty-four years old.

Consuelo told us her baby died down in Haiti and wept bitter tears and so did her friends until we learned she didn't have a baby in Haiti.

Lovette wants to be noticed, too, and she has learned the easiest way for her. She's the loudest whore on the block. She verbally seduces every male C.O. in the institution, calling out things to make even another whore blush. Having established what she considers a personal relationship with them, she then casually tells them to go fuck themselves if they give her an instruction she doesn't want to hear. She talks very loud and she talks constantly and she says nothing. I sometimes wonder why she hasn't bored herself to death.

Sitting in the hall outside a friend's cell is her favorite place to perform. That way she is sure to be heard by at least twenty-nine other women. One night she stood in the hall, arms in the air over her head, swinging her hips with a bump to the left and a bump to the right while she bellowed out, "Ma father says this," bump. "Ma father says that," bump. "Ma father says this and ma father says that. Ma father says this, and ma father says that" over and over again, with no sign of letting up.

Finally I went out in the hall. "Stop it, Lovette. Stop it! You've made this corridor untenable for everyone, for days. Now it's time to stop." Her response was the usual, "Who the fuck you think you is. You got a number just like me." I sometimes think if I had a nickel for every time that has been said to me in the past seven years, I'd have enough money to start a new life.

I asked her quietly, "Are you going to perform like this next week when your children come?" It struck a nerve. "I can behave with my kids any fuckin' way I want!" "Do you love them that little?" I asked, and walked back to my cell. There was quiet for a moment and then the chant began again, almost in a whisper. "Ma father says this and ma father say that. Ma father says this and ma father says that." In a little while it stopped.

She said to me the next day, "Did you notice I been quiet, Mrs. Harris?" in a tone half fresh, and half asking for approval. "Good," I said and kept walking.

One of the many tragedies in here, perpetrated by employees of the taxpayers, is that many of the C.O.s enforce only the rules that are easy, convenient or amusing to enforce. The kind of structure and security that many psychotics require is missing. Rules change from day to day and if they don't, the officers do. And it isn't just psychotics who need the structure. We all do. I'm willing to concede, after seven years of empirical study, that rehabilitation is a vague pipe dream that people should define before they talk about doing it. But training is something else. We can be trained, in constructive ways, or permitted to continue to practice destructive ways. The latter is easy. The former takes time and patience.

The rule book, handed to me the day I entered

prison, says, under General Rules, rule 1: "Obscene language will not be tolerated." In fact, obscene language is one thing that is always tolerated. I sit in my cell sometimes and jot down the sounds of the corridor verbatim. "You tell that motherfucker somebody fuckin' with you and he don't give a fuck." "That ain't no fuckin' way to talk to no fuckin' body. You ain't got no fuckin' discretion." The language of Bedford isn't White English or Black English, or pidgin Spanish. It's Fuck-Speak with the volume on high.

One ordinary evening, when obscenities had rung out in the corridor for several hours, a C.O., a polite and pleasant man who had been standing in the hall while the show went on, came to my cell door to say, "Good evening," and chat for a moment or two.

After the amenities and the weather had been covered I said to him, "You know, I'm puzzled. The first rule of this place is that we not use obscene language and yet you've been standing out there for twenty minutes, listening to them and saying nothing.

C.O.: Well I can't say nothin' to 'em unless they're talkin' direct at me. They just sayin' in general, so I can't say nothin'.

Jean: That isn't true. The rule clearly states obscenities, meaning all obscenities, are not permitted.

C.O.: Well, I can't deteriate to that when it's indirect. I'm only one spectacle here. You can't go around savin' the whole world. I try to just keep it livable. I think one's safety is more secure than being verbalized. I do have priorities.

Jean: Would you want your wife or your daughter to talk this way?

167

C.O.: I can't change 'em all. I can't tell 'em all what they could do.

JEAN: You don't have to tell them what they can or can't do. Just tell them they're too good to sound the way they sound. Tell them: You're better than that.

C.O.: Well, you gotta remember, these women come from all walks a the country. I try to keep a stern, lean atmosphere, to curb the worser things they do. Everybody deserves betterment of life, but you cannot think what you cannot say.

I thanked him for stopping by.

Fifteen

The history of childhood is a nightmare from which we have only just begun to awaken.

DE MAUSE,
THE HISTORY OF CHILDHOOD

"Are you my mother?" the little boy asked.

"No, honey," Dorothy said, "Your mother is over there. See the lady in the yellow blouse, smoking the cigarette? That's your mommy."

"Are you my mother?" the child asked another stranger in the visiting room.

"I don't know who your mother is, dear. Maybe the ladies in the Children's Center know." Dorothy had forgotten the child might not know what yellow is. She took the six year old by the hand and led him to his mother. They hadn't seen one another for four years, and there had been no communication at all. Now mother would be leaving prison soon, and the sister who had been raising the child was ready to "get rid of him." The child was bewildered by the visit and the mother was too.

"What do you do with a kid that age? Jesus, he's runnin' all over the place." Her answer was to leave him and have a cigarette. Whatever bond of love should have helped hold the difficult moment together wasn't there. They were two

total strangers suddenly being told "you belong together."
We watch that scene frequently in here. Happily just as
often we watch a child who has seen mother once a month
for two or three years run from the entrance of the visiting
room all the way to the end of it, throw herself into mother's arms, and remain glued there for the whole visit,
laughing, talking, sharing jokes, sitting quietly, knowing
the connection hasn't been broken.

Keisha told me one day after a whole week of summer
visiting during our special Summer Program for inmates'
children, "Oh Jean, it was beautiful. We had time together. She's just got her period and I could sit close to her
and hold her hand and explain all about menstruation to
her. I know she wanted to hear it from me. I hated the
thought of having to tell her over the phone. You know
what that means to me? God. Just to say to her 'you gotta
get your hair cut' means we're still connected. I'm still her
mother."

Some women believe "getting stuff for the kid" is what
mothering is about. "My baby gotta get the biggest and
the best," was Claudia's constant refrain. She is a large,
raw-boned woman who professed undying devotion to her
beautiful infant son. "Naquan gotta have shoes," she began
demanding when the baby was six months old. Telling her
shoes would not be good for his tiny feet so soon made no
impression. "They tell us that shit so they don't have to buy
shoes. My baby gotta have shoes." While she lived with
him here in the prison nursery, Naquan had the biggest,
best and most of everything. That his possessions were the
product of her own ego trip is something she probably
doesn't know. Three days after Claudia left prison, her
baby in her arms, she dropped him off at the home of a
casual acquaintance and never came back.

Dawn is six years old. She was born to her young
mother, Monica, here in prison. For a year she lived with
Mother in the prison nursery. Then she went home to
Grandmother and Grandfather. They brought her twice a
week to see her mother and kept pictures of Monica all

over the house and spoke of her lovingly. Grandmother died a year later and now Dawn lives with Grandfather who continues to bring her to prison but only during school holidays and weekends now that she is in school. The loving relationship of this mother and child is as strong as any mother-child relationship could be outside, perhaps stronger, because each moment together is precious to them both.

Cora is a battered wife who killed her husband. Her relationship to her twelve-year-old daughter saddens me. Tracy is brought often by nuns to see her mother. Instead of hugging her and using the time for playing a game or just sharing togetherness, mother invariably finds something wrong. There's a button missing on her coat. There's a tear in her blue jeans. Whatever it is, mother sits stoicly mending during the visit, with very few words passing between them. Cora is too busy "being a good mother" to love her daughter. She doesn't really know how. She has been little loved herself.

There are many hurtful intrusions into the lives of these mothers and children so one cannot point to each sad case and say, "Aha, no bonding," and yet the difference between the mothers who will spend the rest of their lives trying to maintain or rebuild all the broken fences of their family relationships, and the mothers who only go through the motions of what they suppose is mothering, is easy to see.

In Donna's case, brain damage has come between her and her four children. She hadn't seen her ten-year-old son for five years when he came to visit last week. His school counselor brought him because he kept expressing a desire to see his mother, and his father, with whom he lives, would not bring him. What went through the heads of these two sad strangers as they met in a prison visiting room only they know. They didn't kiss, they didn't touch. They said, "Hello," and looked down at their feet. They wandered into the Children's Center and mother stood there while the boy looked over the toys on the shelves. Neither one knew what to say, so they said almost nothing.

171

After forty minutes of awkward, desultory talk, Donna said, "Well, I gotta go now. I got things to do." Mother and son walked to the gate where Mother would leave him.

"Are you going to give Mother a big hug?" the C.O. asked. The child reached out and Donna stepped back.

"He's too big for huggin'," she said and turned and left.

She was proud that she had the visit and proud to show the flowers he had brought her, but the visit itself left her feeling frightened and helpless.

"Don't worry, she'll hug you next time," the C.O. said to the child. He wants to come back.

I like to believe the children are still survivors. It is far more often that Mother is the emotionally detached, the walking time bomb. The children, most of them who come here at least, still reach out, still react to the need for attachment, or seem to. What goes on inside them heaven only knows. And then there are those who just stop coming.

Infants and children of inmates make up the darkest part of the story of crime, yet they are the only source we can count on for light in the future. It is a well-established fact that what happens to us in infancy sets the scene for the rest of our lives, sets it, quite possibly, indelibly. To be accurate, I should go back to the fetal stage, not start with birth. For many humans, infancy itself is too late. The drugs and liquor and cigarettes and candy bars some mothers have indulged themselves and their unborn babies in, the milk and fruit and grains they didn't feed them, can be the beginning of a very troubled life. If Mother's drugs were administered with dirty needles, birth itself can be little more than a death sentence. Yet, it is true in America today, and in many other countries where we have withheld drastically needed funds, that while we insist upon the birth of a fetus, we do tragically too little to see that the fetus is healthy, and that someone in its world is waiting and able to take good care of it, or

172

even give it a place to live. So many of these small people die in the preamble of their lives.

I don't live with the myth that everything can be resolved, that every problem has a solution, but I believe each of us should have a fighting chance to work out our own resolutions, not be thrown from birth into the inevitable disaster. Lack of needed care, both prenatal and postnatal, for millions of American children is one of the reasons many of us now live comfortably with the myth that rich people have smart kids and poor people have "dumb" ones, and "dumb" kids often end up as criminals, and ain't it a shame? As Anthony de Mallo wrote, "When reality clashes with a rigidly held belief, it is generally reality that is the loser." But we haven't time for that anymore.

There are many men and women who have devoted their lives to studying infants and children, to discovering how and when we humans learn and what the needs of a healthy human being are. Their findings have been widely published over the past forty-five years. Unfortunately social research often has little effect on social policy until the sky falls down. The productive forces of our society are too often disassociated with human needs. All of which explains why today we have plenty of places for the rich to live and play and a frightening shortage of homes for the poor. Does that have anything to do with crime? You bet it does. When you live on the street, you become a street person.

It was studies made of youngsters who were sent away from bombed areas during the Second World War, to the country outside London or to Canada or to Australia, that began the intensive studies of the effect on children of separation from parents. The general conclusion of those studies, published by the World Health Organization in 1961, was that it would have been healthier for the children to stay and take their chances with their parents.

Dr. René Spitz, writing in 1946, was among the first to tell us that "it will be necessary to take into consideration in our institutions, in our charitable activities, in our social legislation, the overwhelming and unique importance of adequate and satisfactory mother-child relationship during the first year of life, if we want to decrease the unavoidable and irreparable psychiatric consequences deriving from neglect during this period."

Those "irreparable psychiatric consequences" have been recorded thousands of time in juvenile courts and they are recorded in here too. Again and again there are three basic qualities glaringly absent in the psychopath: the ability to trust, to empathize and to form affectionate relationships.

It is the mother living in poverty who may be too disturbed to give a baby the nurturing it needs. There may be too many other children to share her attention; there may be no husband to help her raise the children. She may have had a mother as distracted and untutored as she herself is. The way people live, the way they relate to one another and the way they treat their babies show up only too clearly a few years later when those children go to school.

Dr. Burton White writes in his major work, *The First Three Years of Life:* "To begin to look at a child's development when he is two years of age is already too late." Dr. Ruth Benedict, the world-famous anthropologist, tells us in *Patterns of Culture* that "from the moment of his birth, the customs into which an individual is born shape his experience and his behavior. By the time he can talk he is the little creature of his culture."

Konrad Lorenz was one of the first to observe bonding in animals. Dr. John Bowlby was one of the first to point out the importance of bonding between mother and child. Selma Fraiberg in her book *The Magic Years* pointed out something many of us still do not acknowledge, the relationship of learning to our capacity to love:

. . . We have learned that those mental qualities which we call "human" are not part of the constitutional endowment of the infant, are not instinctive as are the characteristics of other animals, and will not

174

be acquired simply through maturation. The quality of human love which transcends love of self is the product of the human family and the particular kind of attachments that are nurtured there. The quality of human intelligence which depends very largely on manipulation of symbols, especially language, is not simply the product of a superior mental and vocal apparatus; it is achieved through the earliest love attachments. Man's consciousness of himself as a being, the concept of "I," of personal identity — the very center of his humanness — is achieved through the early bonds of child and parent.

Masaru Ibuka, founder and former chairman of Sony Corporation, who began the study of how children learn many years ago with the birth of his son, may have said it best: "The early development of a child is not to produce geniuses. It is to educate a child to attain a flexible mind, and a healthy body, and to be bright and gentle."

I find that a lovely thought, to help our children be "gentle." Rich and famous are our adjectives of choice. How splendid if they could be gentle. That word for me today carries with it a depth of meaning that comes close to wisdom. There is so little gentleness here.

A White House conference in 1970 on early childhood education concluded that the number one need of American children and families was quality day care. The result of their report was the Comprehensive Child Development Act, sponsored by Representative John Brademas, now president of New York University, and Senator Walter Mondale and passed by Congress in 1971. It was vetoed by President Nixon, after a powerful lobbying and hate-mail campaign was mounted to defeat it. One of those credited with killing the act was Mrs. Phyllis Schlafly, a woman who preaches with great conviction that children should stay at home with mommy. Unfortunately, she ignores the reality of mothers who go out to work, mothers who are too sick or too spaced-out to be useful to a child and mothers brought up by a mother also too spaced-out to be useful to a child and therefore never has learned what mothers do. There is no way to say what difference the act would have made in the lives of nineteen and twenty year olds today if it had been in place and administered for the past seventeen years. I find it ironic that Mrs. Schlafly has, on more than one occasion, been voted one of the ten most admired women in the United States.

In an experiment to demonstrate the hypothesis that early training and education can have a powerful effect for good, even on children born to mentally deficient mothers, doctors in Milwaukee took forty infants whose mothers had IQs of less than 75, and put twenty of them in special day-care centers at age three months. There they were carefully nurtured with adult affection and attention and stimulated with toys and interesting surroundings. By the time they reached school age their IQs were all over 100. Not one child was retarded. The other twenty children had an average IQ of 85, and 60 percent of them were judged retarded. That report was published in 1987.

Findings in a study in Ypsilanti, Michigan, that lasted twenty years and followed children who had been in a Head Start program and a control group that had not been in it, found the Head Start children to have better job records, to have graduated from high school in larger numbers, to have more often married and to have far fewer criminal records than the control group.

As John Bowlby, one of the pioneers in the study of bonding between mother and child, put it a good many years ago, "We are beginning to know what is good for children, but we still don't do enough to teach parents and persuade communities to help them provide it. . . . A child who doesn't show an enduring attachment to one particular person is likely to be severely disturbed. . . . In time, some children simply stop reacting to the need for attachment. They cut themselves off and push away the

176

person who shows concern. The whole range of feeling and desire for attachment is gone. Without doing it consciously, certain types of information are shut off. The emotionally detached child is a walking bomb."

I'm sorry to say the only babies born here to Bedford mothers that I have heard or read about in later life, I read about in *The New York Times* when all three of them, males, had committed serious crimes and were headed for long prison terms. But in each case, the mother was addicted to drugs or liquor, had given them up to foster care and their young lives had consisted of one denial of love after another as they moved from one foster home to another.

One of the boys had killed a six-year-old girl. Asked if he felt sorry about what he had done he answered, "Why should I feel sorry? I didn't even know her." How much more detached than that can one be?

The fate of these young men does not establish that a prison nursery is a destructive place to be born, but rather that either we should keep the children longer or have facilities for them to protect them when they go out.

In a recent article in a national newspaper, some correction officers and Family Court members were quoted as saying that judges are apt to be especially lenient with pregnant women and mothers of young children and to avoid sending them to prison. Statistics don't corroborate that. At any one time, at least 65 percent of the women in this prison are mothers and two-thirds of their children are under ten. The number of pregnant women in jail and prison in the United States is estimated at between 7 percent and 10 percent of the total. The number of pregnant women at Rikers Island as I write this is fifty. The number of babies in our nursery at this moment is twenty-nine. The median age of the children who come to our Children's Center is seven, and we average over five hundred child visits a month.

It is the overwhelming evidence of so much research as well as my own empirical observations here that cause me

177

to endorse so strongly the prison nursery here at Bedford. I am familiar enough with our nursery to know it has many problems, most of them I think because the young mothers are not adequately counseled or supervised while they are here. But the babies leave here at age one for the most part beautiful, healthy, bright, sociable youngsters who have had a loving start, something many of them might have missed on the street. Many are also able to go home with their mothers, since the average sentence here is under three years.

With its nursery, its children's program, a visiting room that is open seven days a week from 8:30 A.M. to 3:30 P.M., and forty-six-hour trailer visits with one's children and legal spouse, Bedford unquestionably does more to acknowledge the importance of the mother-child relationship, and the importance of maintaining family ties, than any other state prison in the country. A current study, just completed, of women's prisons in this country, corroborates that.

There are many lawsuits all over the country now in progress against prisons and jails that fail to give adequate diet and health care to pregnant inmates. The care given to them here is like almost anything else, very good some days, terrible others, depending upon which staff member is on duty. Obviously on the whole it is adequate as the babies themselves attest to it.

Gloria told the nurse she was in labor, that her other children had been born very quickly and that she should get to the hospital. The nurse on duty assured her she was wrong and sent her back to her housing unit. Ten minutes after she was locked into her cell for the night, her baby was born. Since, by law, infants are to be born outside the prison, the same nurse helpfully cautioned, "Don't cut the cord. The baby's not born until the cord is cut. They can do it in the ambulance."

Laverne wasn't as lucky. She begged to be taken to the hospital, but she, too, was told it was too soon. Her baby, when she finally got to the hospital, was stillborn. The doctor said it had been dead only a short time.

There is no question that the prison does far more than the reformatory did to keep mother and child together. Until the past ten or fifteen years the mothers were encouraged to make plans for the babies to leave after five or six weeks. Not all did, but many did. Adoption was far more prevalent until just after the Second World War than it is today, which is a mixed blessing since some of the mothers, both white and black, in and out of prison, now keep clinging to children they aren't prepared to care for and too many children are cheated out of living a healthy life. With one out of sixty-one babies now being born in New York testing positive for the AIDS virus, I would hope that some time soon, until we have a cure, we decide that men and women with AIDS should not be permitted to have children. If you have once seen an AIDS baby, weighing eleven pounds at fourteen months, looking like one of the children of the Sahel, I think you would agree that is compassion, not cruelty.

Today, unless there is concern about a mother's physical or mental state, or strong reason to believe she will never be the child's caregiver, young mothers at Bedford may keep their babies with them until the child's first birthday. Most do. If they are to be paroled within eighteen months of the baby's birth, the baby may stay with them that long, thus sparing the infant unnecessary trauma. One young mother, chided by another because she wasn't taking good care of her baby and giving it the attention it needed, was told, "You oughtta give that baby up. You're not takin' care of it like you really cared about it." The other woman looked at her and said, "If somebody else wants her, they can have her. If the price is right." The baby should have been removed on the spot, but she wasn't.

At Bedford a public nurse gives the pregnant women a required course in prenatal care of mother and fetus. Two specific courses in parenting are also offered before or after the baby is born; neither of them is presently required, but both should be. The mothers desperately need training.

Mother and infant live together on one floor in the medical building, without the constant counseling that should be provided by the state, and without the needed consistency in nursery rules. To list all of the things that could make the program better is pointless. Some, like screens on the windows, and a washer and dryer, are promised, have been promised for months and even years. Can you imagine a nursery with twenty-nine babies in it in the year 1988 that hasn't — and has never had — a washing machine and a dryer? We were promised repeatedly that when the floor had been rewired the washers and dryers would be forthcoming. Now we are told that a booster is needed to make the water hot enough and that it could be years more before they get it. In the meantime, Mother carries all her clothes and the baby's clothes, too, in a plastic bag over her back, a good city block away, uphill, to another building to do the wash. Having no washer nearby she needs many more clothes for her child than you and I did for our babies. Apparently somebody out there thinks this saves money. The average housewife would lose her mind at all the pointless waste in here.

With or without a washing machine, the program exists and that is the first big step. The Department of Corrections does not list it as a priority, but the prison administration is wise enough to know that this nursery is important to the babies, not a way to indulge the mothers. In fact the young mothers are the only prisoners living two in a cell, sometimes even three in a cell, under conditions that are often extremely frustrating, especially for a young woman who has just experienced childbirth. Perhaps Governor Cuomo's newly declared Decade of the Child will inspire the Department of Corrections to look more carefully at what can be done for the infants of inmates, so they don't just replay mother's role. The important thing is our babies leave here, for the most part, bright, healthy beautiful babies. They've had a decent start with a good deal of loving attention.

Janice Warne, who was superintendent of the facility in 1972, did her best, as other superintendents before her had done, to keep the baby count low. "Frankly," she said, "I like to get the babies out of the institution as soon as possible. It's healthier for the child. . . . More inmate parents are taking the babies now. Previously only foster homes or adoption was open to them. The mother will have a difficult time getting the child back," she admitted, "but Social Services in the community are now much more understanding."

The true value of the nursery to society as well as to the babies has never been scientifically evaluated. Several people have asked to do an in-depth study of the children, following them even after they leave Bedford, but without funding they soon move on and the study comes to little or nothing. Dr. René Spitz's study made in the 1940s (not at Bedford) is the best and only serious study I know of that compares infants at birth and one year later who had spent that first year in a suburban home, a poor rural home, a hospital nursery (not unlike our boarder babies of today) and a prison nursery.

Tested at birth for awareness and infant responses, the suburban children tested highest, boarder babies next highest, rural poor next and prison babies last. A year later, the prison children had shown the greatest growth, the hospital children had regressed, the suburban and rural children had stayed about the same. The boarder babies were in a well-run hospital nursery, clean, warm, with the babies well fed, but the staff was assigned eight babies per nurse, too many children to give any one infant all the holding and rocking and loving an infant needs to learn to feel at peace and safe in her or his new world. Until Spitz had studied many infants and recorded his studies on film — heartbreaking film — it was widely believed that an infant could not die of loneliness. Indeed it can, and many have. And some who survive the loneliness can be damaged for life.

In a recent article about separation and bonding in a

women's prison in North Dakota, the warden was quoted as saying, "Bonding is a good thing in a good family setting. But I don't know what value it has for these kinds of people." That's about as intelligent as saying "humanness is all right for nice people, but I wouldn't want to see it in criminals." Someone must take care of a child and a mother, even in prison, if she is to be the child's main caregiver, is the logical one for the infant to bond to. Fortunately, or unfortunately, our babies don't check our credentials. The North Dakota warden added, "She [the mother] needs to learn about herself, to avert herself from her criminality. She needs to learn a work ethic, good habits. She won't learn anything lying around nursing a baby all day." There's no time in a woman's life when she learns more — about herself, about responsibility, about human needs and her own strengths — than while she is caring for a baby and working to support the baby as well. I don't recall "lying around" to do it. The warden should "avert himself from his ignorance about women and babies." Unfortunately, he is in the majority of those who make judgments about prison nurseries. The result is there's only one in this country.

In Europe, where there are far fewer criminals per one hundred thousand citizens than in the United States, fewer young children living below the poverty line per one hundred thousand and far fewer pregnant teenagers per one hundred thousand, there are prison nurseries. In Germany, which gave us the kindergarten, in Italy, which sent us the Montessori system, in Belgium, which gave us the Cuisenaire rods, in France, England and the Scandinavian countries, there are prison nurseries.

At the main women's prison in Rome, the Ribibbia Femminile, nonviolent mothers with their babies may go home on weekends, and trained nursery nurses are employed to play with the babies and teach mother and child. Here at Bedford the C.O.s assigned to the nursery floor have no special training for the job. Some are able, some don't even like babies. "Tell your kid to shut up," I've heard one tell a young mother with a three-month-old baby.

Preungesheim, the mother-child unit in Frankfurt, Germany, women's prison is probably the outstanding prison nursery in the world. It employs teachers and social workers to help the mothers learn how to become good mothers. Children are permitted there up to the age of five, with the building designed to keep the children separated from the rest of the prison and to give them plenty of opportunity for outdoor play.

I must confess I am torn as to the wisdom of that many years, and yet I have seen five years on the street destroy some beautiful children. Infants grow older, only older, mind you. They don't grow up unless it is required of them by a loving adult who assists them in the process. For many of these children the loving adult is missing, or the loving adult hasn't grown up herself. I have watched the metamorphosis of a pretty little girl of nine into a sullen hooker of fifteen. It is an ugly and unnatural thing to watch nature working backward, the butterfly destroyed before it even spreads its wings.

I have watched a child who could read any book in our Center library at seven come to visit now in stiletto heels, tight dresses that wouldn't even look very good on a thirty year old, lots of eye shadow and a cigarette in one hand. She's on the pill now. Even all those books didn't save her. She stopped thinking they mattered. I look at this girl and wish I could wrap up the childhood she's missing and give it to her for Christmas. She's twelve now.

Sixteen

"All them women always braggin' about what they got. Ain't one of 'em got a son like mine. He so smart he even surprise me. He got new shoes, and a red and white shirt, and blue pants, and he look good, and his hair ain't nappy, and he smell good too."

An inmate's role as mother is the most difficult one she has to play in prison. About two-thirds of the mothers were living with their children and were their principal caregivers when they were arrested. For the other 33 percent, out of sight has been out of mind for a long time.

Unfortunately the public often reverses these statistics and pictures most female inmates as poor mothers. For good or for ill, it is the children who have to decide that. There are many very loving mothers here who suffer the tortures of the damned because they are separated from their children. There are some very unlovable women in here whose children love them anyway and need them very much because they have no one else. There is nothing sadder than the women here who were raised in foster care, one home after another, who today haven't a single person out-

184

side to call, to have visit, to receive a package from. And the only place their children can go is into foster care to start the cycle again.

You see and hear every shade of the maternal rainbow in here. "I used to get high every day, but I check every day to see my gramma got my kids first. That's why my gramma say, 'I'll always take care a your babies 'cause you always so careful 'bout the babies before you gets high.'"

"I haven't had a date since I got paroled, Jean. I just want to be with the kids. I feel as though that's the only thing I'll ever really want again, not to be away from them. Not to have to wonder where they are."

"My son hasn't talked since I came to prison. He's four years old now and all he'll do now is grunt."

"I been pregnant four times. First one I had an abortion. Second one lives in California with his father. Third one I give up for adoption. Fourth one my mother's got. I'll tell ya. One kid is enough. I sure learned that."

It is hard for anyone to know the nature or quality of a woman's relationship with her children before she came to prison. The child's apparent happiness at seeing her means something. But mother herself, after months away from the children, often imagines it is far more ideal than it was. If she was using drugs regularly outside, the weeks and months in jail or prison may be the first time in a long time that she has been "down" long enough to realize what she has done. What percent go back to their children and do their best to be mother again no one knows. There has never been a follow-up study of any consequence of the women who didn't come back.

Their children, all unwittingly, often tell us more about life with mother than mother herself could.

Two children in the Center asked us one day if they could put on a puppet show. We have some fine hand

185

puppets and said of course they could. They couldn't seem to agree on a story to do together so they each chose two puppets and made up a random conversation between them.

Nine-year-old Jake went first. "What do that woman want? She got all I have. Got ma money. Got ma furniture. Got ma welfare check. I'm asking ya Charlie. What else that woman want?" The conversation went on in that vein for a moment or two with Charlie shedding little light. Then, as suddenly as he asked to perform, he stood up, took a bow and moved over for the next child.

Another day two little three-year-old girls were playing in the house corner. One child bustled about arranging the doll's cradle and dressing her baby. The other busied herself over the stove. "I got the baby, Maime. I'll put her away safe. Won't let that man see the baby. That man ain't goin' touch my baby. He got no right to see my baby." Maime's problems were different. "Ma husband is drivin' me crazy. He always want chop liver for his dinner."

It isn't difficult to see how even the very young pick up such conversations. When husbands, common-law or other, are mentioned, more often than not it is with little affection. "I gotta letter from my daughter's father today. His wife left him. Ha! I told him if he thinks he gonna get my daughter I'll kill him first. I done it before and I can do it again. I'll kill the motherfuckin' bastard. You know what he ask me? He wanna know do I got a man in here. I tell him, Whatta you think? Shit—course I gotta man in 'here.' " She probably thinks she is a loving mother. I think it's fair to generalize that poor mothers are often more possessive than middle- and upper-class ones. "They're mine. Mine."

The fear of what the cost of separation will be, and how long it will be before she can find a job and a place to live for all her children, is on many of the women's minds. Becelia said to me one day, "It's going to be war when I get back. How do I handle it when I've been gone so long? Whose decision is my daughter supposed to respect? Mine or my mother's? It puts so much turmoil on the kid. I can be in control. But that's not enough. I've changed these five years, but she's changed, too. I've got to get to understand her needs all over again. It's sick to be away so long. It's crazy to put people through it. They don't think about what it does. They just don't give a damn. Look at Edna. Look what happened to her, the trouble she had. Her own mother took her to court. She thinks those kids are hers now. You gotta go back and live at home. You're lucky if you got one you can go to. And you don't want to rebel or act like you didn't appreciate what your mother did. But you don't want to be belittled either. For five years you've been told you're nothin' but shit. Now you got to learn how to be a person again and you gotta feel like one, too." In this case, the problems proved more than Becelia could cope with. She went back to drugs, though she hasn't been returned to prison. Too many do return to it. Her daughter is still in school and more than surviving. She's one of the strong ones. Such kids are heroes.

One of the most moving things the mothers do for one another in here is share what they have learned about separation from their children, and ways they have discovered to make it less painful for both. There are problems unique to an incarcerated mother, beginning with, "How do I tell my child I'm in prison." Separation is a subject always covered in our Parenting Through Film course and added to the Red Cross course I teach as well. Since there are no films on the subject, different mothers, usually ones with very long sentences, take the class and share, most generously and openly, though the subject is painful. We have now made two videos of our own on the general

187

subject.

Kathy Boudin, who played a role in the Brinks hold-up tragedy, has a twenty-years-to-life sentence. So does her husband, David. She has taken the class several times—each time most movingly. Their son, Chesa, was fourteen months old when they were arrested. "He was born feet first," she told us, "so we gave him a Swahili name that means "dancing in the light." What a happy beginning.

"I don't focus on what I'm missing," she said. "I try to make here and now, the moments he can visit me, as full and real as possible. It takes a lot of strength, the struggle to keep our relationship real."

For the first two years of her incarceration, she was in jail, not prison, and she was not allowed to touch Chesa when he was brought to see her. "You touch that baby, the visit's over," she was told. After the first visit she decided he couldn't come again. Not touching him was too painful. Two months without seeing him was more painful still, and she asked her parents to bring him back. This time Chesa didn't reach out for Kathy. He turned away and acted as though she were a stranger. She was devastated, but determined that whatever the future held, she would begin, somehow, to build a relationship of love and support with her son.

Before prison, while Kathy was in jail, Chesa wasn't allowed to have any toys with him during the visit. He brought a little piece of colored yarn one day, and the guard took it from him. Undaunted, now only two years old, he turned to the wall and used that as his toy. One moment it was a refrigerator from which he took food for his mother. One moment it was a television set and he and his mother could sit and pretend to watch it together.

"I tried to think of a way to be connected to his life, and tried as I do every day, to be aware of what stage he is in. And finally I began making books for him."

188

She showed us some. They're simple and lovely and they will always be important in Chesa's life. "Here is one about color. They're so simple to do. Any magazine will provide the pictures. Here is a walk in the woods. I try always to make them relate to something happening in his life. Here's a book about my cell, and one that Judy Clark wrote about a nest outside her window, building the nest, then the eggs, then the hatching."

Kathy has made Chesa a zoo full of stuffed animals, of whatever small piece of fabric she can find, a fairly primitive collection since sewing is not her strong point. But Chesa loves them and always reminds her before a birthday or special occasion what animal he wants next. The latest one is a skunk. She is tireless, playing imaginative games with him, asking him endless interesting questions, giving challenging answers and options to his questions.

"As he grew a little older I tried to relate more to Chesa's own experiences and the serious losses in his young life. We've spent a lot of time dealing with his attitude toward my being in prison. Before that I was so freaked out about losing the experience of being with him I couldn't think in terms of what had happened to him."

When Chesa was four, he began having tantrums and becoming very withdrawn. He spent his life visiting between jails to see his parents. He began to have psychological counseling, which was helpful. It gave him a neutral corner where he could talk about the things that bothered him. Given blocks in the psychologist's office, he always built a jail. He talked about how to escape from jail, too, and where he might live if he escaped. For a while he went through a violent stage when every game had weapons involved. "Let's play house. Choose your weapons. I choose a gun and a knife."

Chesa lives today with friends of Kathy's who share

her political and social convictions, most of which I have never heard her discuss, but which I'm afraid I would find difficult to understand. As a mother, I understand her and admire much that she does, and understand her human mistakes, too, the ones that are always easier to see in others than in ourselves.

"We wanted always to be honest with him, about everything. Maybe we told him too much too soon. It was hard for him to understand the permanence of where he is. He still asks, 'Well when you get out, where are you going to sleep? Should we get another bed? Will you sleep on the floor?'

"We told him right away that we were in prison. He asked, 'Why are you in prison?' and I told him it was because of our political principles though he doesn't know yet what this is. He visited his father one day and David told him we had been wrong to both be arrested. Next time he came here he said, 'David said you made a mistake. Why didn't one of you stay with me? You're stupid. You're really stupid.' "

For a while during their visits, Chesa was consumed with the frustration of knowing his parents had been wrong and admitted it. They didn't both have to leave him. One afternoon, during the Children's Summer Program when we were allowed to take the children out on a terrace, Chesa climbed a small tree and began throwing twigs and leaves at his mother. "I hate you!" he cried to her. "I hate you, I hate you. Why did you both have to leave me?"

"It isn't over," Kathy said. "It will come again on a different level."

Joan said, "I know. My son kicked me. He said, 'You left me and I hate you.' "

Kathy and Chesa sit and read stories together when he is here and she reads to him over the phone. He always calls her Kathy and the woman he lives with "Mother." "It was very hard to accept that, but it's best for him," she said. Once when she called him, he said to her in an excited voice. "Kathy, put down the phone and go and see the sunset. You won't believe all the colors." She ran to a window and looked and then went back to the phone to express her pleasure in a shared experience. "You're looking at the same sunset I am, aren't you?" Chesa asked. "The very same." "Then if we can both see the same sunset at the same time it's almost like being together, isn't it? And we can see the same moon, too."

The other women listened, deeply touched, and recognized new ways to reach out to their own absent children. No one can understand the feelings of an incarcerated mother but another incarcerated mother. We were sitting in the rec recently talking about our children. Regina said, "When I call my Julie she always says, 'Mommy, let's play memories.' Memories aren't enough for an eight year old, but she always sounds happy when I say, 'All right, remember the time when you were only three and you and Suzie and I . . .'"

I should add that the feelings of hurt and longing for our children has nothing to do with their ages. They never go away. I see my grown sons walk into this terrible place, and the joy of seeing them, combined with the pain of knowing this is not the place they should ever have to enter, never goes away. It uses me up inside.

I try always to be very upbeat, to tell them the funny things that happen, to talk about them, but sometimes I don't succeed. When they came last Christmas morning to see me, I said to them, "Do you realize this is my seventh Christmas here?" Jim smiled, "Correction, Mother. It is our seventh Christmas here."

Everything bad that happens to her child while she is in prison, a mother thinks wouldn't have happened had she been outside. Much would have happened anyway, because of the nature of the life-style where so many youngsters are growing up. Lydia's eleven-year-old son was arrested for selling crack. Bonnie and Rissa, twelve year olds who come to visit their mothers, and who still like the little-girl toys in the Children's Center, are both on the pill. Phillip, Tanya's son, is in second grade. His teacher found a knife in his desk. Tanya said, "It's all my fault. I was just tryin' to teach him how to protect himself. He ask me, 'Momma what I suppose to do when the big boys get after me?' I told him, 'git you a bottle or a knife, and they won't bother you no more.' I didn't think it through right. I shouldna told him that. I see that now." Darla's son and daughter were signed up for the Summer Program but couldn't come. They were both in Juvenile Detention two weeks into their summer vacation.

Patty was murdered on a Friday night. She was stabbed to death by strangers in an elevator. She lived long enough to get to her father's apartment and say, "They cut me, Papa. They cut me," and died in her father's arms. She was fourteen.

Many of us knew Patty and cared about her. She took part in our Summer Program for inmate children for three summers. We saw her grow tall and handsome with all the makings of a young model. She was full of life, and like most fourteen year olds, afraid of nothing, comfortable with her own immortality. Her mother has fifteen more years to serve for conviction of murder.

Is this the way God squares the account? Maria thinks it is. Her grief is multiplied by guilt. "Oh God," she moaned, "If it could only have been me. Take me, God. Give Patty back." Her face was a portrait of grief, hers and the faces of all the women who sat near her, patting her knee, rubbing her hand, joining their sobs with hers.

How one grieves is a cultural thing, I guess. I remember Jackie Kennedy, swathed in black, walking tall and silent to Arlington. Being strong while the whole world watched was a matter of pride. Here we mourn in many ways, with silent stoicism for some, with high-pitched cries and shouts of protest for others. I watched Maria that night and hoped someone would give her something to help her sleep. They did. The C.O.s were deeply moved and very kind to her.

Matilda's son was killed in a small village in Colombia and she didn't know it until two weeks later. I can still hear her howl of pain as she stood in the hallway, the letter in her hand. There was a fight after a soccer game, the letter said.

For a little while she consoled herself that the letter was a lie, that someone was trying to hurt her. "He's alive. I know. She's a wicked woman that one who wrote the letter. I knew she was a bad woman." Later, when she knew it was true, the loud choking sobs began again.

Gloria's daughter was killed by a truck. Carmen's baby died of AIDS. Lila's baby died during a heart operation. Candy's baby drowned on a picnic with his foster parents. Marlene's brother went to the store on a Sunday morning and was shot to death by a holdup man. Ellen's eighteen-year-old son was chased up over the curb by a car and crushed against a wall. Betty's nineteen-year-old son was shot in the leg by a fourteen year old who held up the store where he worked. He had nine operations and finally the leg was amputated. Dawn's sister was shot in the head when she opened the door one morning. Gloria's son died of a heart attack. Giselle's mother, cousins and uncle were murdered in their home in Medellín, Colombia.

One would expect to live a lifetime without knowing of such agony. Here violence and death are everyday fare. Barbara's two brothers were shot and killed within a year and a half of one another. Her husband was shot to death five months later. She never cries.

She never complains. It is as though she were programmed for tragedy. Wanda's brother died in prison of cancer. She didn't know until one of her letters came back stamped "Deceased." The constant presence of death in the lives of many prison women is one more thing to separate them from those who judge them. I can think of nothing more unnatural, nothing that leaves God with more explaining to do, than the loss of a child.

No one hears more of these tragedies or does more to try to alleviate the pain of them than Sister Elaine. There are days when the sadness in her eyes is too painful to look at. "They have the wrong name here," she'll say. "This is the House of Calvary, the House of Sorrow." And you feel something on those days, a whole new thought you have never expressed before, something Lance Morrow calls, "The terrible, moral power of woe." It doesn't fit comfortably into the value system you've been so comfortably smug about for a lifetime.

Seventeen

It's one thing to see the land of peace from a wooded ridge . . . and another to tread the road that leads to it.

ST. AUGUSTINE,
CONFESSIONS

"Fuckin' honkies" is a popular epithet for white C.O.s in here. I am "an old white bitch." "Old" is usually their choice of the most stinging adjective. This is not to suggest that I am a constant target in here because of my age. Not at all. By and large we get along very well, these young black women and I. Many of them go out of their way to help me carry heavy things, to share a pot of spaghetti with me or their favorite dish of rice. They have been taught from childhood to respect old people, especially grandmothers. Some of that respect for age is rendered to me, and I am a grateful recipient, though frankly I don't feel old at all, except during those moments when my heart acts up. When it does, they couldn't be more solicitous. They give me a feeling of security that someone will be there if I need help.

195

Those who share concern for me, and would like to protect me from any more unpleasant epithets than I have already fielded, would like me to leave out of this book anything about the subject of racism. It would be a fool's errand. There is no way to discuss prisons, or a prison experience, and pretend racism was not there at the scene.

American prisons are monuments to racism, even though the Supreme Court itself seemed to deny this in its decision in a recent case involving the constitutionality of the death sentence. Many statistics were presented to show that we are more apt to give the death penalty to someone who has killed a white person than one who has killed a black person. It was a difficult case with strong convictions on both sides.

The fact is, the rate of incarceration of blacks in this country is six times the rate for whites. Does the law judge blacks more harshly than it does whites? Or are whites just more honest than blacks? There are a good many people on both judgmental teams and still more who don't bother to give it much thought one way or another.

I often hear black women say, "It's harder for us, harder for us to get work, harder for us to be women, harder for us to be mothers." W. E. B. Du Bois wrote:

The negro is a sort of seventh son, born with a veil and gifted with second-sight in this American world — a world which yields him no true self-consciousness, but only lets him see himself through the revelation of the other world. . . . One even feels his twoness — an American, a

196

Negro; two souls, two thoughts, two unrecon-
ciled, striving; two warring ideals in one dark
body, whose dogged strength alone keeps it
from being torn asunder.

I couldn't understand that "twoness" when I first
came here but I feel it now, and hear it, especially
from some of the loudest and most dangerous
women, a seething bitterness, even hatred, just be-
neath the first layer of skin. One woman yells at me
each time the word AIDS is mentioned, "Fuckin'
white faggots give it to the black man." Another likes
to tell me, "Economy of this country was built on
the backs of the black man." But what angers her
more, on TV news at least, is any mention of the
holocaust. "Who the fuck care about all those Jews?"

The night I urged the women to let me watch
"just a little bit" of a special program on the Constitution, I remember that when the subject of the
Dred Scott decision came on, the largest,
and the loudest, woman in the group got up and
turned the channel. She sometimes gives me the
very distinct impression that she would like to break
me in two. I went back to my cell.

There was a moment in a Mercy College class on
Constitutional law when I realized for the first time
the kind of scar that slavery has left on many black
people, even generations after it was abolished.
Whether it's a scar or a blanket to hide all your sins
and troubles under I'm not sure, but it still has a
powerful effect. The mere mention of it among
many of these women is an unspeakable put-down or
the reminder of something they simply cannot handle. I was auditing the class when the Dred Scott
decision came up again.

The professor introduced it as "the worst decision

ever made by the Supreme Court." Suddenly the room, always overheated, seemed cold and tense. Some didn't know the difference between the Revolutionary War and the Second World War. But somewhere the name Dred Scott rang a bell for each woman there, a warning bell. Now he was going to talk about slavery and they did-not-want-to-hear-it. "But I thought you'd be particularly interested," the teacher said. "It's about your own people." "We heard enough a that shit," they told him. "We ain't listening to no more." He looked a little shaken, summarized the decision and went quickly on.

It isn't enough to point out that somewhere down the road everyone who came to America came from a different culture and had adjustments to make. Blacks have been more isolated than any other minority group for longer, which has encouraged them to cling harder to their own distinctive culture. That's fine up to a point, but people who want to get ahead in mainstream America, black or white, have to work hard at it and sometimes have to sacrifice the things they most like to do. "Making it" is getting harder.

Over the years I have read many books and articles about why the disadvantaged minority child tests lower, drops out earlier and in larger numbers, has more illegitimate babies and goes to prison in larger percentages than whites. Invariably the reasons given always point the finger at our failed educational system, "which doesn't understand the black child, doesn't appreciate the blacks, and is oppressive to the poor."

The black child, they tell us is more loving, more emotional, strong on intuition and feeling, weak on reflection and analysis, brought up in homes where body language is the primary means of communication, not the written or spoken word. This may be true, and may even have its charms, but you can't read a book with body language, nor can you read the technical manual needed to fix an air conditioner or a word processor.

Many of the youngsters who come to our Children's Center, three and four years old, have already memorized rap songs. LL Cool Jay is the new Mother Goose. Fair enough. Much of the real Mother Goose was spawned in political doggerel, not in lullabies. Everyone praises them and is highly amused. But then if it's good enough when you're three, why not when you're seven or even twenty-seven?

The National Council of Teachers of English was not doing anyone a favor when it issued a manifesto saying, "Kids have a right to use their own language. Standard English is in no way superior to any other English." In a vacuum, a good case can be made. In the real world, such nonsense makes for chaos. Unfortunately the more we tolerate chaos, the more we get. Anyone who has lived through the past twenty-five years in America must acknowledge that. And the people creating the chaos, doing their thing at everyone else's expense, are proving unfit to live even in their own culture.

People who use the word "shit" to replace hundreds of appropriate nouns — "I ain't eatin' this shit, I ain't readin' this shit. I ain't wearin' that shit. I ain't listnin' to no shit" — not only have a vocabulary deficiency, but a perception deficiency, which makes for a very warped view of the world.

So what does it all mean? It means if a child, any child, goes off to school and isn't prepared to use words, and hasn't already acquired a sizable number of them, and has no idea what new doors open when you read a book or have it read to you, is set up, really set up, to fail, if not in the first grade, then in third or fifth, but soon. A tragedy is in the making. Millions have already been made. I live with hundreds of them. Crime starts early and peaks fast.

One of the most damaging things I observe in prison is the underestimating of the black woman — of all of us — but mostly of her. The most insidious put-down of one human being by another is to underestimate them and this we do by requiring little of them. The tragedy is that by the time many women arrive here they think those who require nothing of them are "the nice guys." My enemy is my friend, he gives me an excuse for being what I am — where I am and "all I gotta do is time." Ask them to write a paragraph, they'll dare you to make them do it. Ask them to write ten sentences using a particular word in each sentence, and they may copy them right out of the dictionary or they may knock you out with ten originals that tell you the story of a hard-lived life. Few have any idea of the power of their own words, grammar notwithstanding.

Enough black people have now made their way successfully into virtually all areas of human endeavor to indicate that it is quite possible for others to do the same. What a godsend it would be to the whole country, but to blacks especially, if the people who run the prisons would give prisoners more credit for the intelligence they have left and make them use it. Maybe Katherine Davis, dated as some of her proclamations may sound today, put her finger on the heart of things when she said, "I will take the job if I can run it as a school." And school, whatever all those reformers of the sixties may have written, is not just fun and games.

There is food enough in this country to feed us all. There is free education through high school and still some college scholarships that go begging. (The schools would be better, of course, if we paid teachers more than prison guards and attracted more brains out of law offices and into classrooms.) There are hundreds, even thousands, of help-wanted listings in our newspapers, but cause and effect have stopped being logical. It is not the time for prisons to be packed to bursting and more and more American citizens to be living in the street. Yet that's what has happened.

The national government estimates that there are from three hundred thousand to two million homeless people in this country nationwide. They're hard to count because they're often hard to find. Local ordinances try to keep them out of sight as much as possible so as not to offend those who have a home in Manhattan, another in Armonk, one in Palm Beach, another in Palm Springs and a pied-à-terre in Paris. As the line in a play currently on Broadway explains, "the wonderful thing about the '80s is that you can be greedy and still like yourself."

But it isn't just the five-home families that bear the blame. There's blame enough for everyone. The American family, middle and lower socioeconomic groups as well, must take their share and the reason is very basic. Our families, too many of them, are not preparing their children to go to school and learn. America's schools have been our whipping boy for years. Hundreds of reports have been written, millions of dollars spent telling us how to rewrite curricula, make textbooks simple, make requirement easier, make requirements harder, test the teacher . . . I have read many of those reports. I have yet to read one that says what is one of the most important

201

things we know about ourselves. Infants are born ready to learn. If we treat them badly for their first five years, they'll not make the grade at school.

Neil Postman says, "Schools should not, except under the most extreme provocation, try to accomplish goals which other social institutions traditionally serve." He is absolutely correct. They have, heaven knows, enough on their own agenda. But today that extreme provocation is here, and not only the curriculum, but the school's role must change. There are more children living in poverty in America than ever before, one in five, pushing up toward one in four, and the number of those children who are minorities is far out of proportion to their census number. Thirteen percent of the women in America are black, yet 52 percent of the women in prison are black. Ninety-one percent of the babies born with AIDS in America are black or Hispanic. Seventy-one percent of the women with AIDS in America are black or Hispanic. There are more teenage mothers in America than in any other country in the western world, and a large proportion of them are black. The dropout rate of all our children is too high, but the dropout rate of minorities is over 50 percent. The main cause of death of black males between fifteen and twenty-four is murder. The foster-care programs in our large cities are swamped and some foster children are sitting in waiting rooms by day and sleeping in a different bed every night. There are sweatshops again in New York City, a short walk from Trump Tower. Some of the children I know who play in our prison Children's Center live four and five in one welfare hotel room, for which idiots in the local, state and federal governments pay rents as high as $2,500 a month. I use the term "idiot" for the logical reason that to pay such sums to keep people living like animals, not as well as many animals in fact, is so senseless one can only conclude in all conscience that idiocy is at work.

Many hotel children are too transient to be accepted at the neighborhood schools. Some are driven by taxi every morning to a school far away. Over half don't go to school at all. There are fifteen thousand runaways living on the streets of New York. "Boarder babies" are a new addition to our social lexicon, babies abandoned at birth with nowhere to go from the hospital where they were born. Tens of thousands of children go home after school to empty houses. It's estimated that more than fifty thousand preschoolers nationwide stay home alone all day. Who is playing parent for all these children? Many of their parents have come up the same way. They don't know what a parent is or does. They need parenting themselves.

"What difference do age make? My mother was fourteen when I was born and we got along fine," says a twenty-seven-year-old mother of five as she sits in prison playing an endless game of Monopoly. Eighty-two percent of girls who had their first babies by age fourteen had mothers who were teenage mothers, too. It's now an old family tradition. Babies thus born are often of low birth weight and apt to face many learning disabilities in the years ahead. And the more problems the child has the less Mother will be able to cope with it. She'll soon blame the child for what she did to it.

Until I came to prison, I had never heard the term "parenting." When I did, I thought it was something one taught in prison, only because so many of the young women here said, "I been on the street all my life." They hadn't experienced family life, or "mothering and fathering," the way the American dream says we all should.

But parent-child relationships, once taken comfortably for granted, are now a national concern, and, I'm told, parenting classes have become popular outside of prison, too. All that good stuff that God and your mother once taught you is now on tape.

In the one hundred years between the end of the Civil War and the middle 1960s, American life assumed a pattern quite congenial to the family. The excesses of the industrial revolution went on too long, but there were plenty of jobs for the uneducated and child labor laws finally came. Americans settled in to give their kids a Flexible Flyer and "a good education." To say that we became complacent is the kindest we can be to ourselves.

In all the many times I have heard teenage pregnancy discussed among young mothers here, I have never heard the word "responsibility" used, and I have never heard anyone suggest that a twelve year old does not have a God-given right to be sexually active. Clarice tells us with all due pride that her fourteen-year-old son assures her, "He always use Trojans, and I check to see he have 'em." The cultural teaching of several generations has done its work and trying to save these young people from a lifetime of poverty and ignorance is not being done outside, and it certainly isn't being done in here. I'm not sure for many of them whether it still can be done. But it isn't too late for their young children if we get to work fast.

A social worker, "expert" self-styled, who visited here not long ago announced, "I am not of the rehabilitative mode. To rehabilitate people is to change them, and that would be pompous." Clara said, "Where I live they make you feel like a fool if you're a virgin by the time you're thirteen. I got two older sisters used to tease me all the time. Finally, I told 'em I wasn't one no more, and they let me alone, 'til I got my period and couldn't use tampax and they was at me all over again. Flora said I was a tomboy, and then everyone in my family figure me for a homosexual. They talked about it right in front a me.

"Well, I showed 'em. I had me a baby."

If it is pompous to change this value system, to change the thinking of those who live by it, then by all means let's be pompous.

I showed a film called *Prisoners of Chance* to a class of fourteen young women. It is about teenage pregnancy, with the true stories of three young teenagers. In the discussion that followed I realized the enormity of the task of trying to teach the young the seriousness of the problems that teenage pregnancy can create. In spite of the sadness of all three stories in the film, not one of the women watching it suggested that the teenagers had created problems for which they were responsible. It was the parent's fault, the school's fault, society's fault. The young mother was simply a victim or no one was a victim because nothing bad had happened. Not one of them suggested that the baby might be short-changed. In fact, interestingly enough, the baby didn't figure in their comments at all. Joanna, obviously street smart and tough, said she had a baby at seventeen, she now has three children, and she supports them and herself "throwin' bricks" (breaking and entering). Floretta, now divorced, seemed most concerned about letting me know that she was married when the baby was born. She had done all the socially correct things, but she didn't mention her child.

Finally I said I had reservations about the film because it didn't emphasize perhaps the most serious problems of teenage pregnancy, too many sickly babies born prematurely and the feminization of poverty. I wrote the last three words on the board. "Twenty years ago," I told them, "we actually believed we could wipe out poverty in this country. Today, the number of Americans living in poverty has risen and the overwhelming number of them are women and children." "That's not so," Robin said. "They just say that because women are the ones on welfare. They don't count all the men out there livin' off women on welfare."

If poverty itself were the primary motivation for crime, then the Great Depression would have been the time of our highest level of crime. Beyond bootlegging, which was excessive, this wasn't so. Perhaps that's because the gulf between rich and poor, while very wide, was not something we were constantly reminded of. Americans had the feeling, right or wrong, that they were all suffering together.

The level of expectations created in the hearts of most Americans after the Second World War has, I think, much to do with crime in America today. We stopped wanting equal opportunity and started expecting equal results. We were invincible, we were rich (so we must be smart), we had risen from the ashes of our depression to become the most powerful country in the world, and everyone, rich and poor alike had played a role. Like the Queen of Hearts, we promised ourselves, "Everybody has won, and everybody shall have a prize." In the past week, I have seen advertised $28,000 cars ("only" $28,000), a $1,200 evening purse, a $3,000 doll, a short velvet evening jacket for $14,500, and endless ordinary three-bedroom, one-bathroom houses for $300,000 — not to mention a full-page ad for gourmet cat food and one for gourmet chewing gum. A family of four living on the minimum wage couldn't buy a week's supply of the cat food.

If you've never bothered to check, or had cause to know, the federal minimum wage is $3.35 per hour. If you work all year, forty hours a week, your annual income will be under $7,000 a year. A family of four, according to the same federal government, says you must earn $11,209 a year to keep your head above abject poverty. Does that have anything to do with why single mothers turn to sex and drugs? You bet it does.

Sandra sat with her second baby on her lap in the parenting class this morning and said, "Jean, I didn't want to come back here. I've already been through here with one baby. When I left here, I had the kid and $40.00. I went right to welfare and told them that I needed a place for us to stay. They gave me an address and I went there and it's a big room with plastic mats on the floor, one right next to the other. I wasn't going to stay there with my baby. So I went back to welfare and they gave me another place run by nuns. I get there and it's cleaner, and they got beds, and a nun tells me I'm welcome and I can come in at 6:00 P.M. and me and the baby gotta be out each morning by 7:00. What am I supposed to do all day, carryin' a baby and everything we own? So I call one of my numbers, and I'm back in business, and next day I got a place for us to live. So they caught me, so here I am, all over again."

The women at Bedford want all the good things as much, or possibly more, than you do. They measure their own self-worth, not by what's inside, but what's outside, what shows. The two easiest and most obvious ways for the unemployed or unemployable to make money are to sell sex or drugs, and the rich as well as the poor make a ready market for them.

In the 1960s, in spite of a period of sustained prosperity and federal programs to help the young and the poor, crime began to soar. As James Q. Wilson has put it "American democracy, which seemingly had endured in part because . . . we were a 'people of plenty' relieved of the necessity of bitter economic conflict, had in the 1960s brought greater plenty to more people than ever before in its history, and the result was anger, frustration, unrest, and confusion. . . . The prosperity of the decade was also accompanied by alarming rises in welfare rates, drug abuse, and youthful unemployment. During the 1960s, we were becoming two societies, one affluent and worried, the other pathological and predatory." Today, those lines are drawn more starkly than ever, and it doesn't bring out the best in either group. If there's a "Banana Republic" in the Western hemisphere today, it's the island of Manhattan.

In 1963, President Johnson noticed that a lot of us were not getting our fair piece of the pie and created the Great Society. This program, probably begun for all the good reasons, may have become part of our undoing. It unquestionably changed the value systems of a significant number of our citizens, values that had started changing thirty years before. What was meant as a springboard from poverty became for some the quicksand of self-destruction.

A system of Aid to Families with Dependent Children, AFDC, and usually called "Welfare," which had been established state by state during the depression to help widows, orphans and those physically and mentally unable to support themselves, gradually and insidiously became a way of life for hundreds of thousands of people and, worse still, a pattern of life that someone "out there" owed you.

For a long time, only a woman without a live-in

man could receive AFDC. A woman's economic security now lay, not in a husband—even a working husband, if he didn't rise above the minimum wage—but in having another baby. A thirteen- or fourteen-year-old girl began her economic life, not with her first job, but with her first baby.

When something is done frequently enough within one's socioeconomic class, it becomes acceptable. Children out of wedlock have become the norm in large areas of America, the top of the economic ladder and the bottom, and it's working its way into that last grand bastion, the middle class. Our children experience sex before they know what a subject and a predicate are. We've mixed up the order of things.

Today, at the top of the educational and entertainment ladder, women have discovered they can earn as much as a man, or more, as long as they don't tie themselves down too soon with an apron. Sex is just as available to her as to him. No problem.

At the bottom of the ladder, women have discovered the check stops when the guy moves in, but as long as she gets the check she can attract more men and have more babies and get more money.

Being a "fast breeder," as Lena calls herself, can be a source of income, not enough money to raise healthy, well-educated kids, perhaps, but that's long-term thinking, and Lena doesn't do that. "With my four kids I get as much as my mother does, so what's so bad about that?" Even a job of her own can work a hardship on her because minimum wage jobs often don't provide needed medical insurance for mother and children, and people on welfare pay 100 percent income tax if they start to work: For every dollar they earn, that much welfare is deducted. It is a system which, like prison, takes away anything resembling intelligent motivation to work hard. New welfare legislation presently under discussion may, and should, change this.

When I ask some of the women here why they think women who are already living in poverty continue to have more children the answers vary. Ethel's reason satisfies her: "I'm Catholic." The fact that she is in here for starving her ninth child to death rather than aborting it or using birth control seems to leave her still comfortable with her God. Many of the other women are quiet for a moment, as though they don't like dealing with the question, and then say rather haltingly, "Well, we don't have much that's ours, but the babies are ours. Maybe we need more love than rich people because we don't have much else." The trouble is — what many find out too late — a baby is born ready to learn to love, but it must first be shown what love is. And learning this big lesson requires a good and loving teacher, more interested in the baby's needs than her own. By the time a child reaches two and is trying to become an independent individual, his or her young "No's" make Mother feel rejected. It's time to have another baby.

Until 1963 black unemployment rates and new AFDC cases rose and fell together, as was to be expected. Then the illogical began to happen. By 1973 nonwhite unemployment had fallen to 6.5 percent and new AFDC applications had risen by 222 percent. A report written a few years earlier by Daniel Patrick Moynihan, then assistant Secretary of Labor, now a senator, warning of the rising number of black women who were raising and supporting children without the help of husbands, was not well received. At the time, the report was called "racist." Today, he has updated the report and Congress is scratching its collective head trying to figure out what can be done about it. The gap between rich and poor in our country has grown wider during those years and American industry is feeling the consequences of not enough well-educated citizens to hire.

William Wilson is a brave black sociologist and head of the Sociology Department at the University of Chicago. He has recently written a book entitled *The Truly Disadvantaged: The Inner City, the Underclass and Public Policy.* Wilson points out that the number of black men earning $25,000 or more annually and the number of black men earning $5,000 or less annually are both growing. But the middle-class blacks have now moved out of the ghetto and taken their clubs and shops and churches with them. Only the very poor are left behind. The space between black and black has become as great as the space between black and white. It is economics, he writes, not racism that keeps the lower group down. If he could observe the racial hatred in here in C.O.s as well as inmates, he might qualify that.

There are many people who disagree with Wilson but it seems a positive step forward if all blacks could begin to believe that they hold their futures in their own hands, instead of having to stand help-lessly waiting to see what someone else does to them. Wilson also notes that the loss of thousands of well-paying industrial jobs that required little or no education and the increase in highly sophisticated jobs that require a good deal of education play a greater role in the desperate straits of many poor people than racism.

One hundred years ago fewer than 3 percent of our citizens went to high school. That's one of the reasons it's so easy to be misty-eyed about what a great job they did. You didn't need a high school education to live a useful, productive life and to support your family. Today, the demands on the human brain are greater than they've ever been before. It's easy to give up if all your friends are doing it too, and you haven't grown up with loving, self-confident parents who have assured you from the cradle that you were up to whatever the test might be.

We know that many families, and many women alone, cannot give their children this kind of start in life, so it is incumbent upon us, the national family, our schools, our day-care centers, our public and private facilities, society as a whole, to do the job instead. And the work should be shared by the brightest and the best of our young graduates, college and high school both, chosen as a great honor to serve the young and the future of our country for a year or two.

There aren't many writers, especially black writers, echoing Mr. Wilson's thoughts at the moment. It might be helpful to some of the women I know if there were. Many of them here are potentially more intelligent and useful than they would have us know or even admit to themselves. In seven years in this prison, I have heard only one officer who loved them enough to tell them so. Most C.O.s simply parrot the same sounds, the same values as the inmates, or tell them when the doors will open and close. I can still see Sergeant D. Williams standing near the officer's bubble, short, stout, feisty, and caring, saying to the women, "Look at you. You should be ashamed of yourselves. Lazy! Dirty! Using foul language! Living in filth! There's no excuse for this. Don't tell me your excuses. I came up the same way you did. You had all the same chances I had, and what did you do with them? Now clean up your talk and clean up yourselves and go back and read the rules of this place. And if you can't read, I'll see you get into class where you can learn."

At that moment, though she certainly couldn't have known it, an old white woman standing nearby loved her.

Williams gave a damn. She talked to the women as though they were her children, not as though they were not worth bothering with, only worth sharing a few four-letter words with. "Don't feel sorry for yourselves," she said. "That's too easy and too destructive. Get up and improve yourselves, even if it's just a little bit."

Williams has retired now. She is missed. She knows the secret of being a lady. It takes guts.

Eighteen

*"We teach reeling and writhing of course to begin with,"
the Mock Turtle replied, "and the different branches of
arithmetic — ambition, distraction, uglification and
derision."*

LEWIS CARROLL

In 1970, the restructuring of New York's correctional system was begun and the distinction between reformatories and state prisons was abolished. What had been happening for years was now officially recognized. In 1974, the so-called reformatory sentence, by then an indeterminate minimum with a four-year maximum, was repealed. A few weeks later, after having been enforced for more than eighty years, the reformatory sentence was declared unconstitutional by the U.S. District Court of the Southern District of New York. Giving everyone the same sentence whatever the crime finally stuck in someone's craw.

Though many people preferred the bucolic sound of Westfield State Farm, the name of the institution now became Bedford Hills Correctional Facility. Abby Hopper had urged those in charge not to call it a prison, but at the same time she urged that it not

214

be a prison. Today, I imagine she would say, "At least be honest. Call it what it is." December 1981, Commissioner Thomas Coughlin III stated in a sworn affidavit, "The Department is no longer engaged in rehabilitation and programming efforts, but rather is forced to warehouse people and concentrate only on finding the next cell." The situation today is even worse. Bedford is a prison warehouse, whatever its name may be.

By 1971, the women prisoners were now all to be housed on the reformatory side of the property, where three, three-story prefab buildings were put up, all connected by long corridors. On the ground floor are kitchen, dining room and offices; and cells for 360 inmates are on the second and third floors. Men from Rikers Island were now to be housed across the street where the women's prison had been. For two years the two prisons were headed by one superintendent. In 1972, they were separated and the men's prison is now called Taconic, a minimum security prison. Word today is it may soon be emptied of all the men and be used for women again. The prison business is so successful it is in a constant state of expansion and rearrangement.

When I arrived at Bedford in March 1981, a new one-story building for segregation and protective custody was going up (the SHU building). The cells of that building are apparently the last single cells that will be built here for a long time, if not forever. New single cells now cost anywhere from $10,000 to $100,000 and are rising. At the rate we are imprisoning people, at those prices, we would have to stop building schools and houses and roads and just concentrate on cells. Hence we are now taking over ferry boats, hospitals, troop ships, anything with four walls and a door, and turning them into prisons.

The last two hundred beds to be added to Bedford

Hills Correctional Facility are two years old and are in four separate areas with fifty beds per area. The cost was $4,000,000, a mere $20,000 per bed, but then they are not in cells, only cubicles, in which one can easily be observed at all times by neighbors on both sides, and which cannot be individually locked, not only because they have no doors, but because they also contain no toilet or running water. Women who live there describe nights of musical beds while women creep about to join their lovers and friends, and couples go off together to the shower, even sleep, together in bathtubs. It makes for a fine, healthy "correctional facility." Had we updated our medieval parole system and made use of the many legitimate alternatives to prison for nonviolent people and thrown out our state law which requires that if you commit a second felony, even shoplift or write a bad check you must spend at least a year in prison, we wouldn't need two hundred more beds. To me, the worst part of the cubicles is that more than half of them are "inside areas," that is with no windows, fresh air or natural light enough to read by; in short, they are in one sense a throwback to Auburn Prison of 150 years ago.

Turner Building, once an old reformatory cottage, has been recently refurbished into an instant slum, with two floors with rows of beds and no cubicles at all—just bed, lockbox, bed, lockbox—but the areas *are* bright with windows. It is a toss-up as to whether Turner or the new dormitories provides the worst housing in the facility's history—going back to 1901. Turner is not considered permanent housing and is used just for entering inmates until they are medically cleared. But the two hundred new cubicles are "permanent housing." One could spend twenty years in one of them. To put two hundred street women into dormitories where anyone can go in or out of anyone's cubicle, or in and out of shared showers and toilets, is to invite a sexual orgy that won't stop. The women know which C.O.s on night duty fall asleep at what time and which C.O.s play the street games with them, and nightlife is lived around them. There are women there who would give their souls to be moved and some who think it's the best ticket in town. Prison dormitories are a step back toward Newgate and anyone in the prison business knows it.

Asked whether or not reformatories were a failure, many criminologists would answer with a resounding "Yes." Actually, they were an honest, if naive, experiment and as such were not totally without redeeming features. Their efforts to humanize the treatment of female prisoners had mixed results, but certainly today no one would consider chaining women to a wall with their toes barely touching the floor or requiring her to shovel coal three hours at a time or even to slaughter pigs.

A continuing concentrated effort to distinguish between the mentally ill or defective and the knowingly criminal might have left us in a stronger position today to know who should be punished and who should be treated. For the most part today, we just punish. The greatest problem for Bedford Reformatory was that the rules were changed early in the game, and the kind of young women it had set about to reform were soon a very different group than was sent there. It's one thing to run away from home and quite another to steal or kill to support a drug habit. It is quite another thing, too, when issues of race are introduced. And today, as it was from 1910 on at Bedford, you may be sure race plays an important role in all of our prisons.

Today, according to Sections 136 and 137 of the Corrections Law in the State of New York, the Department of Corrections is required to assess a prisoner's "physical, mental and emotional condition," and his or her "educational and vocational needs" and "to provide each inmate with a program of education which seems most likely to further the process of socialization and rehabilitation, the objective being to return these inmates to society with a more wholesome attitude toward living, with a desire to conduct themselves as good citizens and with the skill and knowledge that will give them a reasonable chance to maintain themselves and their dependents through honest labor." I think it is safe to say that there isn't a prison in the State of New York that fulfills the letter of the law, or even comes close for most inmates, in part because not enough is offered, in part because what is offered isn't required.

Granted the word "wholesome" may never be an appropriate adjective for many women here, however many flowers she grows or even how many books she reads. But prisoners can be trained if our expectations of them are high enough and rules with that in mind are consistent enough. Certainly in two or three or five years, they can be trained to get to work on time, and that's a start. And most could be trained in some marketable skill, but they aren't.

In every piece of writing I have found concerning this facility, dating from 1892 to yesterday, there is some mention of how essential it is to teach a woman to support herself at an honest trade. Katherine Davis spoke of "nontraditional roles for women" in 1901 and how it was important for "the girls" to begin learning them.

A 1912 report on the State Prison for Women at Auburn shows a continuing concern for the future of inmates as seen in the following quote:

Many of our women are young enough to profit by a course in Manual Training if it could be provided for them, and find profitable employment when released. At present the only employment open to them is domestic service. A course in domestic science would fit many of them for positions who are now only capable of doing rough, heavy work at low wages, and the course in sewing and dressmaking which we will enter upon in the future, will equip many for making a livelihood at agreeable, remunerative employment that will leave no excuse for resorting to dishonorable means of obtaining both the necessities of life and some pleasure and recreation.

In 1920 a New York prison survey took a hard look at all the "domestic" training at Bedford, Albion and Auburn and called it "busy-work." It recommended vocational training as well as domestic training and acknowledged, as Davis had done, that women, too, must make a living. Nothing happened.

In 1927 another report was made, similar to that of 1920. Yet, as new industries were recommended, they were quickly turned down in Albany, all but the stereotypical female pursuits. "Printing is a man's industry," "Pottery requires men to lift the clay," "Producing dental goods requires too much skill and application," "Tobacco manufacturing is inadvisable for women's institutions." Power sewing, laundering and farming were always approved. Within the facility itself there were also very set ideas. "We wouldn't put a drug user in a beauty culture course" and "a girl from a rural area would not secure a job in the garment industry."

The first federal prison for women was built in 1927, the result of the work of Davis and other women reformers. It was built in Alderson, West Virginia, and named the Federal Industrial Institution for Women, but in spite of its name it offered the same stereotyped work: homemaking, farming, sewing and "care of helpless animals." When women reformers called for more industrial training they were told by the United States superintendent of prisons, "We will never have factories for women offenders. You would object to them, and all of the women in the country would object to them." Apparently, minds haven't changed at the top, because in spite of much talk, except for sewing and answering some phones for motel reservations and motor vehicle inquiries, there still isn't an "industry" in women's prisons. None of the above is currently at Bedford. In California female inmates can also be taught "firefighting," and in Kentucky women can learn to drive a truck.

By 1933, at Bedford women were offered a course in Successful Living taught by the chaplain with the same old familiar standbys: beauty culture, cafeteria service, child care, cooking, domestic service, sewing (only near the end of her stay to prepare her for a job in the garment district), laundry operation and gardening. Volunteers also came in during the 1930s and gave monthly birthday parties, as one would for little children. It was while Averell Harriman was governor of New York in 1958 that industrial sewing was stopped because prison labor was "unfair competition" for honest workers on the outside. Today this remains one of the big unsolved puzzles of prison administration and state and federal legislation. Is it better to forbid prisoners to compete with labor on the outside and send them back into society still unable to make an honest living, or let them compete and send them out with a better chance of "making it?"

By the early 1940s women in the prison at Bedford, the lucky ones, were offered industrial sewing to fill their idle hours. They made sheets, pillow cases, dresses and nightwear. Except for five women with particularly responsible jobs who were were paid 2¢ an hour, the women earned 1¢ an hour and worked 34½ hours per week. Inmates in men's institutions were paid a minimum of 5¢ an hour and could rise to a maximum of 30¢ an hour. The Department of Corrections brochure, published in 1950, added, "It has been recommended for a number of years by the prison administration and the Commissioner of Corrections that the rate of remuneration at the women's prison be raised to a level more nearly approximating that paid the male inmates."

In 1965 a brochure about Bedford listed the same "vocational" opportunities that existed in 1933. In 1972 Janice Warne, the superintendent of both the men's and women's prison, sounded optimistic about the new public interest in prison, sparked by the terrible uprising at Attica the year before. "Our main interest," she announced, "is in developing vocational training and expanding job-training courses for men and women alike." She started a coed course in creative writing which met three nights per week and was very popular. There was still no industry. At the time she supervised 330 women and 280 men.

Warne also announced she hoped to set up a display booth for inmate handicrafts. Some handicrafts were locked in cabinets in the entrance hall when I arrived in 1981 and may still be there, but nobody knows what prices are being asked and no one seems to know where the keys to the cabinets are. We have also been told for several years there is to be a handicraft shop outside the prison gates, but it hasn't materialized. The late 1960s brought classes in key punch operation, which are still offered. We've also been promised a printing shop for six years. The machinery has been here for three years. It has just

221

been plugged in.

In my wandering through *Corrections Magazine* and Department of Correctional Services publications, I have found articles about more than forty different skills available to male prisoners in New York State, among them welding, sheet metal fabrication, lathe operator, drill press, dental technology, optical technology, auto body and auto mechanics, small engine repair, wall and floor tiling, carpeting, tailoring, shoe and leather repair, upholstery, air conditioning (install, repair, service), printing and lithography and others. Only printing is available at Bedford. We're told the reason is lack of money. How much would it cost to teach us how to make a slipcover or to upholster an old chair? When Mrs. Phyllis Curry was superintendent and I had recently arrived here, a group of us pointed out the torn and tacky condition of the chairs and sofas in the recreation rooms and offered to slipcover and repair them if she would provide the fabric. Her answer to us was, "I think it's better if we have them done professionally." Needless to say, they've not been done. Efforts to bring in donations of fabrics are discouraged at every turn. Since C.O.s wear blue uniforms, the color of blue is contraband here, which makes a certain amount of sense so as not to encourage anyone to disguise herself in blue and escape. The result is if a small piece of fabric is sent to us with a tiny blue flower, or a very thin blue stripe, in short a mere dot of blue somewhere in it, it is sent back. The same is true of an orange flower, or an orange dot because the C.O.s wear orange raincoats. Anything left to individual discretion here is hopelessly mired in nonsense.

In fact I was told once that a copy of *Corrections Magazine* was contraband because the security department had figured out that inmates might read the advertisements in it for locks and chains and other prison hardware and figure out how to open them! I've read it recently because a copy was sent me by the editor with a request that I consider writing an article for it. I declined, because of the tone of the request.

A newspaper article of April 1975 was headlined, "Prison Offers Women Industrial Skills." The smaller print said, "Vocational and industrial training for women is severely limited. Where there are more than fifty industrial programs for men, women are largely limited to cooking, beauty culture, and clerical work." It also added, in keeping with the headline, that Sears was about to begin an auto repair course at Bedford, to which twelve students at a time could belong. The program, after a few years, died a natural death, I'm told, because of the women's lack of interest. I'm not sure I believe that, but at any rate it isn't taught anymore. The most valuable offering given at Bedford today, in my opinion, was also begun in 1980 and called "building maintenance." At first, it involved nothing more demanding of the inmate members of the program than changing fluorescent bulbs and hanging bulletin boards. But the women's competence soon became apparent and now they do full maintenance, plumbing, electrical work and carpentry. It's not unusual to watch an inmate standing by a staff plumber and explaining to him what has to be done. Inmates still cannot be licensed for the trades in here, nor can a woman with a thousand hours of beauty parlor under her belt be licensed, but they can certainly be prepared for the tests outside.

Sister Elaine thinks the most valuable program given here was offered by Citibank. Certain approved inmates were paid while they learned how to be bank tellers. Women who finished the course were given a job in the bank when they left prison. The program lasted for four years and then was discontinued. As far as everyone knows, the women worked well and some have stayed to rise to more responsible jobs. No one robbed the bank. Why the program stopped, no one seems to be sure, but some think it had to do with a change in policy of the bank's directors or some of the customers might not have liked it—not good bank public relations.

While one law seems to open the door to vocational training in prison, others close it just as fast. In a study made in 1984 of eight maximum security prisons in New York State, including Bedford Hills, the Correctional Association of New York concluded that 24 percent of their total population was completely idle, and still others were partially idle, that is assigned to unnecessary, unproductive jobs. The Department of Corrections itself reports that 10 percent of its population is idle at any one time. I think that's a very low estimate. Whether slopping dirty mops up and down prison corridors is considered gainful employment I don't know. It shouldn't be.

The nation's first prison work-program started at Auburn 160 years ago. Convicts were leased to private companies. That ended when reformers complained that it was exploitative. Perhaps it was, but I'm not convinced it was worse than letting people sit all day or shuffle about starting arguments or playing pinochle for hours on end.

Until 1979, Federal law in this country prohibited the transportation of prison-made goods across state lines. That's one of the reasons making state license plates was such a popular prison industry. In 1979, the Justice Assistance Improvement Act amended that prohibition, and authorized the establishment of seven Free Venture pilot projects in five states, mostly in the Southwest, to allow private industry to become actively involved in prison industries, either within the prison grounds or outside, with prisoners going out each day to work. New Free Venture projects have since been added. Unfortunately, even if understandably, these projects are strongly opposed by labor unions. They take jobs away from "honest guys" and they make for unfair competition, because the inmates are paid low wages—high for prison—but low for the competition outside.

In New York State, the state constitution as presently written precludes the state from entering into a Free Venture arrangement. Where industry does exist in New York prisons, the products are sold under the trade name Corcraft and used within the prison system or other state programs. However, Governor Cuomo's administration is preparing legislation at this writing, spring 1988, that would permit Corcraft to sell to nonprofit organizations outside of New York, and to the federal government. I can't think of any legitimate reason why the tax payers, federal, state and local as well, should not be given a few breaks at the expense of inmates they feed, clothe and house at horrendous expense. Like so many other things, it's fine if it's honestly administered.

New York prison industry, presently active in fifteen state prisons for men and hiring three thousand inmates, makes all state prison furniture, sheets and towels for prisons and for shelters for the homeless, furniture for state offices, school lockers and most of our prison clothes too. Though it was a money-loser until recently, last year Corcraft, under the leadership of a woman, claimed a $7,000,000 profit from sales of $60,000,000. In the three years ending in 1982, an audit by the State Comptroller's office estimated that our prison industries had lost $16,300,000. When your workers are paid $.95 an hour in a labor-intensive field it's a little difficult to figure out how to lose money until you realize that it is only in the past four years that prison workers were allowed to put in as many as six and one-half hours of work per day. Before that, with all the constant security interruptions, they worked three and one-half hours a day though their supervisors were paid for eight hours. Today Corcraft has arranged with private companies to help them design new products with an eye to expanding and being able to hire more inmates into productive jobs that might open doors for them outside. It sounds good, but then it sounded good in 1912 too. And there is still none of this good stuff at Bedford.

I've asked many women here what percentage of the women at Bedford they think leave with a marketable skill. The consensus is 10 percent. I think that's high. Many have made an honest effort to further their education and have finished their GED, but stopping there does not prepare them for much that they couldn't have done anyway. Not enough, from what I observe, is done to instill in them a respect for many kinds of labor, not just glamor jobs, or what they think are glamor jobs, and big, big money. We can hardly damn them for being like all the rest of us, but it makes for serious problems when they try to "go straight."

Occasionally, when a woman is about to leave and has little education and no idea how she will support herself on the outside, I suggest that she look into maintenance work. I talk about all the new buildings in New York City, the importance of cleaning work, the strength of their union in the city, and anything else I can remember from my two years of working at Allied Maintenance. To a woman they have sniffed at the suggestion, including those who would qualify for good domestic work. "I don't want a job like that," Mildred said. "Think I'll go into add-mini-stration."

There's a good deal of irony in the fact that when

226

cleaning and domestic work was considered as menial a job as one could find, with little pay and long arduous hours, it was the "Bedford girls" who took the jobs. Today, when domestic help is paid at least $10 per hour, most of these young women are too proud to take the jobs, so middle-class college kids fill many of the jobs instead, some working into their own firms, all earning more than they might as a receptionist or typist or some of the other slots that sound more "respectable." I have sat at more than one dinner table where the cook and the butler were making a good deal more money than I was for running a school. I realize more and more each day how many doors are closed to us if we don't like ourselves enough.

Nineteen

"You goin' to commissary?"
*"What for? I ain't got 2-a shit and a window
to throw it out of."*

The most frustrating and destructive part of prison,
in my opinion, aside from being away from family
and friends, is that one is quickly reduced to infancy.
Things that matter are often overlooked. Trifles are
made much of. The commissary is a typical example.
To begin with one can only shop during work hours,
which teaches us that buying stuff is more important
than going to work.

It is difficult to describe the pettiness of a trip to the
prison store. I would have to write a play about it. I
can see the setting clearly.

Everyone will be in blue or green, inmates in
green, guards in blue. Light will come in from the far
right, through barred windows, and house plants will
line the window ledges, not because prisons have window ledges lined with house plants, but because they
will be the only living things in the play that make

sense. Everything will be measured against them, and their behavior. "She has the brains of a houseplant" will be warm flattery in my play.

The passage of time from the beginning of Scene One to the end of Scene Three will be fifteen years. The slow drip, drip of stupidity will begin to leave smooth places on the skulls of the actors, and a constant wind of nastiness will blow the shutters of their sanity, banging back and forth against their brains. But only a few in the audience will know.

It is a tale told from the bottom of a garbage can, or a room in which the ceiling is where the floor should be. It is a tale told from a child's sandbox, but it isn't a tale for children. They would interrupt before the first scene ended. "The emperor isn't wearing any pants," they'd say, and walk away from so much pointless, unfunny nonsense. Happily, they wouldn't know how the play was corroding the souls of the actors.

The commissary is our prison store. It sells some foodstuffs like tea, rice, canned vegetables and fish, sodas, cookies, candybars, soaps and shampoos, paper and pencils, cigarettes and stamps. Inmates may go to this store once every two weeks and spend as much as $60. No more than ten dollars of that may be for stamps. Money in one's account comes either from family on the outside or from an earned weekly stipend, anywhere from $.30 to $.75 per half day's work. Few women have $60 every two weeks, and those who do have a large following of hangers-on eager to carry their groceries for them in return for a pack of cigarettes or a few sodas. They are lionized. At least for the few days before the next buying day they can do no wrong.

Inmates go to the commissary when they are told they may. Before she goes, each woman is given a printed list of what is sold in the store, and fills out her order. As a rule, about one-fourth of what she has planned to buy is "out of stock." It is "on order." It may be "on order" for months on end.

Scene One opens on a prison living unit, cell block, corridor. (They're called all three.) Depending on the day, thirty women, all in green slacks, are trying to determine who will go first to shop. Some days one signs up, some days one lines up, some days one stacks chairs in front of the door to the hallway and the one who wedges her chair in closest to the door goes first. The system depends entirely upon the whim of the officer in blue. It is rare that two shopping days are alike. Procedures change from day to day and even from morning to afternoon.

On a floor where I lived for two years, the officer in blue considered it a matter of honor to change the sign-up procedure at least every other week, and then, when the room was filled with angry, frustrated women, pushing, shoving and shouting invectives, she would step back, fold her arms, purse her lips in a smug little way and say, "Well, you're grown women now. You'll just have to fight it out." No one has to this day told her that this is not what "grown women do."

The suggestion that since all cells are numbered we could easily have a revolving system so sooner or later everyone would be first and each would be last left her looking nervous at the mere thought of such logic and orderliness. How could she go home feeling superior if she hadn't had her fix of human chaos that day — women behaving like undisciplined children, a few like wild animals?

One day she would permit the first in line to sign her own name and anyone else's who yelled out a name to her. One day you could sign only your own name. One day the list was posted at the front of the area. One day it was posted at the back of the area. On more than one occasion, she waited patiently for every woman to sign up, then slowly tore the list into four parts and put the pieces in the wastebasket. "We're not signing today. It's first come first served. Line up ladies," and a wild scramble to the door might leave a few women with charge sheets, locked for five days for "unnecessary violence." "No shopping for you. It's your own fault. You're a grown woman now."

The suggestion that those with a job to go to that morning should shop first left her equally disinterested. The women with the sharpest elbows often have the dullest brains. They plow their way to the head of the line, rush through their shopping and return to the recreation room to play pinochle the rest of the morning. Those scheduled to take a test in the high school equivalency class could be forced to wait aimlessly for another hour.

Scene Two is in a hallway in front of the commissary. A large rectangular hole has been cut in the wall between the commissary and the hallway, with a large heavy metal grating to fill the space and divide the shoppers from the storekeepers, the prisoners from the staff. Anyone who comes in direct contact with prisoners gets "dangerous duty pay."

The commissary has been in two different buildings since I came to prison and it may soon be in a third. The rumor is its present building has been condemned. But then so have other buildings that are still in use. It was moved in the first place partly to enlarge the dining room for two hundred more inmates and partly because it was in an area too readily

231

accessible to inmates. It had recently been broken into and cleaned out, right under the noses of at least six officers in blue. "Geeze, you women are dumb," an officer observed. "If you had any brains you coulda done it years ago."

An officer stands in the hallway at the grating with the inmates and gives gratuitous orders to everyone and anyone who enters the area. She may call inmates and have them come to shop before the commissary staff has approved. The inmate is sent back without any purchases. The commissary staff may call and have inmates sent down before the officer in blue has given her "all clear." The inmate is sent back without any purchases. The pecking order in this highly charged area has never been determined and the tug of war between the two, with raggedy inmate in between, goes on and on.

"Don't stand there. Move over. No. A little to the left. Not like that. More to the right."

"Where's your ID? Let me see it. Don't hand it to me. Put it away. Don't just leave it there."

"Hand it to me."

"Put the blue slip on the desk."

"The blue slip doesn't belong on the desk. Hand it to me."

"Move out of the way. You cannot get in line until the person ahead of you has left the area. I told you! Don't get in line!"

"But she's left the area. She's over there putting her stuff in the basket."

"You do not move to the window until the person in front of you has finished putting her groceries in the basket."

"Even if the basket is on the other side of the room?"

"You heard me. Now, who's next. Line up. Not

there! That's where you get the things. Pass the sheet in under the grate on the left side."

"But we've always put it on the right side."

"Not since yesterday. Now we put it in on the left and pick up on the right."

"Jesus Christ! This place is insane!"

"Who did you say was insane!"

"Nobody."

"Well, watch it. Whose basket is that?"

"It's mine."

"Well you can't leave it there."

"It's where you told me last time."

"I never. Can't you see someone coming downstairs and around the corner could bump right into it?"

"But there's no one upstairs."

"I'm giving you a direct order. Move it. Not there. Not there. Up there. Near the door. Not so near. Over on the side. Who's next? Hurry up. If you aren't in line sit down."

"Do not pick up the bag until your purchases have been passed through the grating. You don't need two bags. One bag is enough."

"Oh oh. I forgot to mark Kleenex. I need a box of Kleenex, too."

"You know the rules. After the list passes under the grating there are no changes. No additions. No subtractions."

"No problem. I can get her the Kleenex."

"Put it down. Don't give her that. Do not give her that Kleenex. She had plenty of time to think of it before she got here. We can't waste time with changes."

"I need the fuckin' Kleenex."

"We're wasting more time arguing about the Kleenex than it takes to give it to her."

"I am giving her a direct order to give that Kleenex back."

"Up yours, you old bitch! Go ahead and write me!"

One customer leaves the area knowing she will be written, locked and God knows what else. An undercurrent of anger murmurs through the women waiting their turn over on the chairs. The murmur will continue and grow louder from now on—

The next customer is called to the window. She has written down thirty candy bars. There is no room on the order sheet to signify which candy bars, so the normal procedure is for the man at the counter to ask, "What kind do you want?" This time he brings a mixture of tired candies that look as though they have spent a long hot summer on the shelf.

"These aren't what I wanted."

"You didn't say what you wanted so this is what you get."

"But you always ask and I tell you."

"I don't have to ask you anything. You don't tell me, you get what I give ya."

"But they're for prizes and the women like peppermint patties."

"Look you're holding up the line. You don't change the order after the paper goes under the grating."

"I don't want these."

"Well you got 'em anyway." Candy bars are 28¢. He rings up 28¢, 28¢, 28¢, 28¢, thirty times.

There's a new man collecting groceries from the shelves to fill the orders. A few months ago he was deputy superintendent in charge of administration. For reasons that are mysterious and only whispered about, he has been demoted from deputy superintendent to steward, to work in the storehouse and now he is putting foodstuff in the wire basket for someone else to ring up. Embarrassment will finally cause him to move on, though changes involving demotion as well as promotion are common throughout the facility. One is rarely, if ever, fired in prison. Only demoted or moved on to break rules in someone else's prison. The new commissary chief has been on board for only a week. Already he is drunk with the power of his new position.

"Let's see your ID. That don't look like you. You're a lot darker than that picture shows. Until you get a good ID picture, you don't shop."

Before the afternoon's shopping is over he has sent twenty-seven women down to the basement where ID pictures are taken and where the backing up of sewage leaves a constant dampness and smell hanging over everything. The inmates mumble audible obscenities as they go, but they go. It takes more than an hour and a half before the whole group has been re-photographed. The guard in charge of the camera is not upset. The exercise breaks the monotony of her day in a smelly basement.

The women go back upstairs. The black girl still looks lighter than she is in the picture. The redhead still looks like a blonde; the woman with her hair pulled straight back will have it curled and fuzzy tomorrow. But they have done what they were told. As they walk back into the commissary hallway, the grating and the window into the commissary are closed.

"It's too late now," the staff person calls out. "No more shopping today."

It will be two weeks before the women can return. They explode with anger and frustration. They howl and shriek.

"Get the sergeant. Get the motherfuckin' sergeant."

"We ain't movin' till we get our stuff."

"Open that fuckin' window."

"Call the lieutenant."

"Call the motherfuckin' superintendent."

"Open the fuckin' window."

"Fuck this shit."

Scene Three is a local A&P. A woman, recently released from Bedford, enters with her daughter. She stops near the door and looks around, frightened and confused by these surroundings. She starts toward the shopping carts, stops, looks around again, tries to move toward one of the aisles, bursts into tears and runs out of the store.

"Mother," her daughter calls after her. "What's the matter? Come back!"

And the curtain comes down.

Twenty

If only Our Blessed Mother had had a girl.
SISTER ELAINE

"Girl, you gotta think about you when you get outta here. What you want. What make you happy. Gettin' a job you like — not one he like. Wearin' nice clothes. Goin' some place nice to eat — shit — no nigger gonna give you that. He buy ya hamburger and then wanna fuck ya to death. You gotta remember, girl. You don't need nobody. You only need yourself."

"I know, Smitty. I know. You're right. I gave him everything. I gave him me and the clothes on his back, and look what he done to me. I'm not gonna need him any more . . . just me and the kids. I'm stronger now. I'm a different woman than when I came in. I'm goin' out there and I'm just gonna need me."

Two women, one white, one black, stand in the kitchen doorway, talking loud and earnestly about how life will be for the one who will be paroled in two weeks, after four years in prison. The talk is brave, but for all its substance they might be whistling down a rain barrel. In four years, Clara has earned her

High School Equivalency Diploma, changed the color of her fingernail polish at least one thousand times, mourned the occasional loss of a "best nail," read an occasional gothic novel, slopped a dirty mop up and down whatever corridor she happened to be on, exchanged street wisdom with ladies in nearby cells, and played Frisbee in the prison yard. Now "the bust" is over and the hardest part begins. Now her four-year-old daughter is eight, and has already been held back twice in school. Now her two-year-old daughter is six and her fifty-seven-year-old grandmother is sixty one and has cervical cancer — her mother is "somewhere on the street," but no one knows where.

Has the feminist movement raised consciousness in this women's prison? The question can be argued pro and con depending upon with whom you're talking. To be a true feminist, in my book, you have to feel good about yourself or be determined to try to feel good about yourself. It also helps to have a healthy mind and body because you're going to be a hard worker and be willing to answer for all your own actions. At that point you've already knocked at least half the women in here out of the feminist ballpark. The true feminists I know have the same gift I envy in successful men. They never seem to tire, and they're always willing to take chances. Sister Elaine Roulet is a feminist in every sense of the word. But then there aren't many of her inside or outside of prison.

In my opinion, the most important effect of the feminist movement on women in prison is that their existence was finally acknowledged. For a long time they were largely ignored and when finally noticed were written about by men. Katherine Davis, Jean Weidensall and Edith Spaulding, whose books were published between 1912 and 1923, were rare exceptions and their work, instead of beginning the widespread study of women and crime, lay dormant for sixty years.

Feminist criticism of academic sexism was almost unheard of before the late 1960s and then it turned not on the sociology of deviance but rather on the oppression of women at home and in the work place.

Some of the inmates who attend Mercy College courses here feel very strongly that their sociology and psychology courses have "raised their consciousness" and will affect them still more when they go out. For many of the other women, feminism is just another middle-class white folks trick. "Has nothin' to do with me." But some of them have been touched by it whether they use the word "feminism" or not. You hear it in the corridors. "I got four kids, and only one of 'em, my daughter, got a daddy, and he's in jail. Father of the first two got shot, and father of my baby die before the baby was born. He used to beg me, 'girl, give it up. I'm afraid I'll lose you. I can take care a you and the kids.' He had a good job drivin' a tractor trailer. But I can't give it up. I want my own money. Men respect me because I don't need their motherfuckin' money. I got my own."

Some people think the terrible increase in female prisoners is an indication that feminism has left its mark. Judges, they claim, are less apt to treat them with special kindness because they are mothers, than they might once have been. "You asked for equality. Well, sister, here it is."

Women imprisoned at Albion prison near Buffalo got a taste of this treatment when a new superintendent arrived. But it was a woman, not a man, who dished it out. "You want equal treatment with men. Fine. You'll get it. Starting now, there will be no more cosmetics on this facility's grounds." It took a lot of arguing, and probably some legal time, too, but they

239

have their cosmetics back. So much of what happens in prisons seems to be unkind or unnecessary or both. I've never come across a book on the philosophy of penology. I'm not even sure there is one.

The doctrine of presumed coercion influenced our courts until the 1950s. This was the presumption that a woman who committed a crime jointly with a man was probably forced to do it. Today the assumption is quite the opposite. "She was probably involved with the guy, and she wanted to be," and women go to prison based on that assumption.

I'm told that some women criminals are more assertive now, no longer satisfied to be the lookout, car drivers, decoy in the con game or the one who cases the jewelry store. Some women are striking out on their own. If this is the result of the work of feminists, it isn't what they had in mind.

One of our more famous inmates, Carol Crooks, came here years ago with a three-year minimum, which meant that with good behavior, she could have gone out on work release at the end of two years. She ended up serving eleven years because of her assaults on C.O.s and on her various women. She still keeps going back to Rikers Island from time to time because of her predilection for beating up women. Maybe the feminist movement has something to do with the fact that her women are now pressing charges. She was something of a folk hero by the time she left, for having assaulted five C.O.s at one time, among other things, and also for having started more than twenty lawsuits against the facility and having won a good share of them. She was a borderline illiterate when she came in, but she memorized the New York State Penal Code and could cite chapter and verse for every legal right she had and every legal mistake the hapless C.O.s made. I used to watch her booby trap the entrance to her cell before she left it or before she went to sleep to be absolutely sure no one got in without her knowing it. She had a special ID that could take her to any part of the entire facility with no questions asked and she crisscrossed the campus constantly with the air of one who's in charge. The night before she finally left Bedford, the C.O.s threw her a party. They thought it was rotten of the inmates not to do the same. "She taught 'em plenty about legal rights in here." I guess a case could be made.

But while the feminist movement may not have made much progress on individual inmates, feminism per se has changed administrative policies. Until 1970 men could be superintendents of a women's prison, but women couldn't be employed in men's prisons. Title VII of the Civil Rights Act of 1964 forbade discrimination because of sex. But it wasn't until the Equal Employment Opportunity Commission held up funding for agencies that discriminated because of sex that a real change came about.

Since women can now serve as corrections officers at Sing Sing and Attica and any other male prison, "turn about's fair play," as my mother used to say. Today, there are not only male C.O.s at Bedford, there are more male than female C.O.s here. It's 8:30 P.M. as I write this, and as usual the two male regulars are on from 3:00 P.M. to 11:00 P.M., plus three male trainees. They're up and down the corridor, all over the place, except the shower room, which they never go in, and which anyone can tell you is where much of the action is.

A few states now have coeducational prisons, which I think are a throwback to something we worked hard to get rid of. But then I'm glad Smith College hasn't gone coeducational, too, so I'm hardly an objective observer. Denmark has a coeducational prison that

241

permits men and women to live in the same cell blocks and permits sexual relations between inmates. As a taxpayer, before we get that humane, I'd rather we sent them all home.

It is with lawsuits that the feminists have left a prominent mark here at Bedford. Two landmark cases in New York State were brought by Bedford women: one, *Todaro v. Ward,* suing for better medical care, and the other, *Powell v. Ward,* suing for due process in punishing prisoners.

The riot of 1974 came first, and within a year after it six major lawsuits were pending against the facility. If they couldn't get what they wanted by rioting, they'd go the legal route, and young bright feminist lawyers encouraged them to do so.

The riot, a short-lived one, began at the end of the summer of 1974 when forty-five women took over the prison and held seven staff members hostage for three hours: four C.O.s, two sergeants, and one nurse. From 6:30 P.M. to 9:00 P.M., having seized the keys, they barricaded themselves on block 112C and D and in the prison yard. Thirty state troopers and C.O.s from Greenhaven, Taconic and Walkill men's prisons all came to negotiate. Carol Crooks, one of the ladies, had been locked for assaulting one or more officers, without what apparently was proper procedure — proper by the books — and this had ignited anything else they were angry about. It ended peacefully, with no one hurt.

Between 1975 and 1982, Bedford became a testing ground to develop a constitutionally acceptable system of inmate punishment that can be used in all New York State prisons. The system presently in use evolved from two federal court suits: the first, when the United States Court ruled that inmates are entitled to some form of due process, including a hearing of some kind, before punishment; the second, after a federal class-action suit brought in the name of a Bedford inmate against the then Commissioner of State Corrections Benjamin Ward. Powell (the inmate) claimed that a punishment given her was completely arbitrary. The United States District Court, Charles Stewart presiding, ruled in her favor and set down specific terms of due process, which the Supreme Court had not done. Inmates, he said, could have a hearing, call witnesses and be given twenty-four-hour notice of the hearing, with a detailed statement of charges and an impartial officer at the hearing.

After the facility's failure to comply in 1980, Judge Stewart held the State of New York in contempt, and appointed a Washington lawyer, Linda Singer, to be "Special Master" to oversee the judge's orders and whether they were complied with. Stewart also ordered the state to pay damages to the inmates for non-compliance, $127,000. Carol Crooks played a key role in determining how the funds would be spent. She polled the ladies repeatedly and then did much of the ordering of the things to be purchased. One hundred and twenty-seven thousand dollars sounded like so much money, she told me, when I arrived, that the ladies were planning to "build a swimming pool, some tennis courts, a track, redo the kitchens on every floor, get color TVs" and a few things I've forgotten. The first purchase made was $10,000 worth of roller skates, which might have been reasonably sensible since even inmates need some kind of diversion and exercise, except that less than a year after the purchase the administration decided roller skating was too dangerous and since then no one has been allowed to use the skates. Anybody want a good buy on some roller skates?

I should add that much of the money went for educational purposes, too—computers and other equipment the state would eventually have had to buy anyway. They came earlier because the women bought them. The whole process of spending that much money intelligently can be chalked up to an eye-opening learning experience.

In 1982 continuing failure to comply with the guidelines the court had established resulted in the summary dismissal of then Superintendent Curry and all of her deputies. They were here on Thursday and gone Friday morning. C.O.s cannot be fired for what seems to me the most egregious behavior. But apparently administration can be tossed out at a moment's notice. It is now 1988, and Linda Singer, at great expense to taxpayers, is still the Special Master in a suit brought fourteen years ago. In spite of this, I am both fascinated and puzzled to read a posted notice which suggests that *Powell v. Ward* may be bypassed if the facility is granted its request to be given the power to place prisoners in solitary confinement for an indefinite period of time without giving them a hearing. It would further permit them to withhold from such prisoners their glasses, dentures, hearing aids and prescribed medication for the first seventy-two hours.

Since the offenses of the last two women I know who were sent to solitary were that one had touched an officer's "left upper arm" and one had written "properganda," it is frightening to think how that "privilege" would be misused. The two women involved in those cases, because they had lawyers, and knew of the Special Master, were quickly let go. But many women here don't speak English, haven't a lawyer and have no idea what their rights are. And many have no staff member to speak in their behalf. I had thought that was the function of counselors, but in both of the above cases a counselor played no role at all.

244

One of the largest and ultimately most expensive cases for Bedford was the suit filed in 1974 by the Legal Aid Society on behalf of twenty-six inmates who charged that the entire health delivery system at Bedford was inadequate to the point of, "deliberate indifference to women's health needs in violation of their constitutional rights." Among other things the suit claimed that a staff doctor being paid for full-time duty worked here an average of five hours a week.

Seriously ill women in the infirmary had no light or call bell and often were left unwatched for hours at a time.

There was little or no follow-up on lab tests, with a potential for dire consequences.

Equipment was out of date and in disrepair and in the words of the deciding judge, "the administrative procedures for medical care were 'grossly inadequate.'"

Medication prescribed before admittance to Bedford was often confiscated and terminated without checking with the inmate's doctor. This included diabetics who did not get insulin. It also included an acquaintance of mine who had muscular dystrophy, and whose family had to sue to get prison doctors to return and continue her prescribed medicine.

Before the case was won, nurses for inmates stood behind a barred, cashier-type window unable to touch the inmate and obviously unable to conduct a useful examination. With this arrangement, the money wasted on a doctor who didn't come in to work could be saved by not having to pay the nurses the extra fee for coming in direct contact with the prisoners. Prison employees who come in direct contact get an extra fee, a little like flight pay or dangerous duty pay, though coming in contact with the women here is not as dangerous as teaching in an inner-city school or driving a bus in New York City. The decision handed down in 1977 by the Federal District Court gave the prison thirty days to work out better access to medical care at the prison. Women won their requests for complete physical exams to be given upon entering the facility and at regular intervals thereafter, prompt examination by a physician for new or chronic ills and immediate examination by a nurse or doctor in emergencies and transportation to the hospital when necessary. The doctor in question was fired, buzzers were put in sick rooms and the nurses' station was opened up so a nurse could actually look down a patient's throat or into her ear, not do it long distance.

Obviously things are better now, but they still leave a good deal to be desired. The women themselves make things harder for everyone, themselves included, by a good many unnecessary trips to the nurse. On the other hand, outside they were free to run to the drugstore for a patent medicine. Here everything except two aspirins or two Tylenol every four hours must be doled out by a nurse and prescribed by a doctor. That makes cramps, indigestion and constipation mighty expensive.

Because any inmate taken to the hospital must be guarded around the clock by a C.O., the expense of serious illnesses is also very high. While I was in the hospital, I had an armed guard next to me even in the intensive care unit though I was plugged into enough extraneous machines to make escape highly unlikely. When I was finally moved up to the prison area of Grasslands Hospital, there were so many C.O.s sitting around with nothing to do that their main occupation of the day was figuring out their overtime.

Dental care has also been improved in the past two and one-half years as the result of still another class-action suit, and any number of individual suits, brought by women whose mouths were seriously damaged by, among other dentists, one who was often not sober enough to be practicing anything. I didn't go to a dentist for the first five years I was here. Having seen what had happened to others, I was far too frightened to go. It is a sad commentary on prison health care that most improvements, at Bedford at least, have come through the courts, the most expensive possible way to accomplish anything.

Still another judgment in the inmates' favor was handed down this year in answer to a class-action suit concerning mental health care here at Bedford. The judgment requires the facility to increase mental health care available to women in solitary confinement, including an initial mental health examination with any appropriate treatment and placement recommendations, an improved system for keeping mental health files and training certain facility personnel in mental health issues. It also requires that a psychiatrist not employed by the state monitor the delivery of mental health care at the facility, for at least the next two years.

But while the ladies have graduated to bringing suits and winning them we haven't won the battle of being taken seriously or treated as men's equals.

Nothing recently published that I know of shows more blatantly the lingering male attitude toward women prisoners, or women in general, than a *New York Post* article of January 27, 1988, headlined, "Women Inmates in for a Shock." "Shock Incarceration" Camps are being set up in various states around the country, for young, nonviolent inmates eligible for parole within three years. They are put through a demanding and highly disciplined six-month program, not unlike Marine boot camp, and upon successful completion of the courses are immediately eligible for parole. This can cut up to two-and-one-half years off their prison time.

Women immediately began asking for a similar course and Thomas Coughlin III, head of the New York State Department of Corrections, has announced there will be one, according to the article, not because the advantages of the program should be passed on to the women, but because if he didn't the ACLU would soon be on his case. Women in the program should be called "Shockettes," he suggested.

State Senator Christopher Mega, Senate Crime Commission chairman, suggested at a hearing that the women be called "Bimbettes," which is probably as cute as the senator ever gets. Should a person who looks upon a woman who has broken the law as a "bimbo" be one who decides what's best for her? It is hardly an intelligent step in that much talked about "building a sense of her own self-worth."

But there is a spark of chivalry left. I read somewhere that in North Carolina it's legal to shoot a man trying to escape from a medium security prison, but it isn't legal to shoot a woman doing the same thing. But the South always did treat its womenfolk better.

Twenty-one

The purpose of a system of law is to provide a measure of fairness in the transactions of life.

JUDGE LOIS G. FORER,
CRIMINALS AND VIOLENCE

I won't write about those women who go out from here before they should, or without the support they need to succeed. Soon enough the media will tell you about them when they commit the next inevitable crime, crimes that people who know them could have predicted. Unfortunately it is always strangers who decide who will go and who will remain behind.

It is those who languish in prison long after they should be at home that the public doesn't hear about, or worry about. You may not even like these women. It's hard to learn and hard to remember that justice has nothing to do with our own personal tastes and preferences. That's why our symbol for justice is blindfolded. Many people just think she's blind and sometimes I have to wonder about that myself.

Maria and Honey are two women who come immediately to mind when you start listing those for whom justice went astray. Stereotypes and stereotyping have much to do with what has happened to them both. I know many women who in the same courtrooms would have walked away, free.

Both Maria and Honey may or may not have done something wrong, but there is a large and totally reasonable doubt that they did anything approaching what they were sent here for. Both cases went to trial, which often adds fifteen years to one's punishment simply for the inconvenience caused or perhaps for the simple gall of saying, "I am not guilty as charged." The punishment given them is draconian and serves neither them nor society in any conceivable way. But then who am I to say? Decide for yourself.

Maria is from Colombia. "Ah ha," you say. "One of those. All those Colombians are drug dealers. She probably got what she deserved." Apparently, even the district attorney didn't agree, because before her two-day trial she was offered five years probation and deportation back to Colombia, where her loving children and grandchildren live and wait for her.

But Maria spoke no English then and apparently didn't understand or wasn't told her options. Her lawyer advised her to take the case to trial although she had nothing to gain and everything to lose by doing so. She had the same lawyer as Connie, another friend of mine who was also talked into going to trial and ended up with the same sentence Maria got—fifteen years to life. Connie's codefendants plea-bargained and were out in three years.

Maria came to prison still not understanding what had happened to her. She is one of the few women here whom I have seen cry, often, more out of fear and being totally overwhelmed than out of self-pity. She is a gentle person, with a quiet manner. She stays to herself, partly because of the language barrier, partly because street people frighten her.

Home for Maria is far away. Her children and grandchildren come to see her when they can, but it's an expensive trip, and they are not in the drug business. When they do come, Sister Antonio meets them at the airport and arranges for them to stay at a convent with her, so they can afford to stay as long as two weeks. Maria lives for those visits. She is very gifted with her hands and she always has beautiful gifts for them when they come: sweaters for all; a doll, which looks like a museum piece, for her granddaughter; stuffed animals for the little boys. She often makes gifts for others when they least expect it. The knitting bag I carry every day, more often with books and paper than knitting, is one Maria made. She quilted a spread for Sister Elaine, and made lovely throw pillows for it — everything made from bits of scrap material that friends send us. Her tastes lean toward pinks and pastels and laces, what we once called very feminine. She also sells some of her sweaters and unique ceramics so that she does not have to ask her family for money while she is here.

Maria's children are the children of her first marriage. That marriage was by family arrangement when she was fourteen years old. She hadn't even menstruated yet. But that is the culture. A woman must marry, raise children and be taken care of, by men. I remember how shocked I was when driving one of the South American girls at Madeira to church one day. For conversation, I asked her what business her father was in. "Oh, I'm not sure," she said. "Something to do with electricity I think." I expressed some surprise that she didn't know. She was seventeen. "Oh," she shrugged. "I don't think even my mother knows." As it turned out, he was head of a large corporation. Women in South America still have "their place."

Maria's first husband was a regular army man and much older than she. She remembers and speaks of him with affection and respect, but by the time Maria was twenty-one, he had died and she was left with three children to raise alone.

Apparently with her family's help and her husband's

pension she did a good job of it. The loving letters and pictures in her cell attest to it. She always shows me the latest pictures so we can both enjoy them and because she is so proud of them.

Maria's two oldest children were married and had children before she remarried. They always came first. She was on a vacation visiting friends in New York when she met her second husband. He was manager of a restaurant. He was also in the drug business, but this he swears Maria did not know. And not a single witness or tape or whatever has ever been produced to indicate that she ever bought, sold or used drugs, or knew what her husband did sub rosa.

They had been married less than a year when the police arrived to arrest her husband for drug dealing. From the moment he was arrested until today he has sworn Maria knew nothing of his drug deals. During her two-day trial, a policeman testified that he had seen her driving the car and dropping her husband off at a diner where drug deals were made. One could drive others all over the city to hundreds of places where crimes are planned and even consummated without having any knowledge of them. One blushes to think what foul deeds may be discussed at 21 or Four Seasons on a daily basis.

On the basis of the fact that she was from Colombia, that her new husband was a confessed drug dealer and that a policeman saw her drop off her husband at a place where drug deals were made, the jury found Maria guilty of "complicity" and she was sentenced to prison for fifteen years to life, which in New York State means she must serve fifteen years before she can be paroled. She had no previous police record of any kind. She has served nine years and has twice been turned down for clemency. She was told by the superintendent, whose job it was to give her the bad news, that she didn't have enough "important people" to write letters for her. She doesn't know any "important people" in this country. She probably doesn't know any in Colombia either. Should this be the criterion

252

for clemency? The facts of her case are fairly simple and can be read quickly. Her behavior in prison has been exemplary. She has hurt no one. There is nothing to be gained by our society to keep her here, since she will be deported whenever she is freed. As her sentence presently stands, the American taxpayer will have spent $500,000 to punish her. Is that rational?

Honey's case is entirely different, and Honey is as different from Maria as two women can be. She is brash, feisty, sharp and funny. She was born in South Carolina and moved with her mother and five brothers to live near relatives in Rochester, New York, after her father and mother were divorced. Whether she was too much for mother or sent back down South to grandmother for her own good I can't say, but until she was eleven she spent more time with grandmother than mother. When grandmother died, Honey moved to Rochester to stay. Her mother worked as a domestic part of the time, and made ends meet on welfare part of the time. She remarried and had four more children. Honey seems to reflect little family closeness or affection. She herself was on her own, "on the street" at an early age. She doesn't look back with pleasure or pride. She is bright enough to know she's better than her past was, and she makes a conscious effort to rise above it. She reads constantly to herself and to the children who visit our Children's Center here in prison. She asks about new words and makes a conscious effort to incorporate them into her working vocabulary. She asks you to correct her and remembers not to make the same mistake again. She writes a great deal, too, and hopes to get a recent article published. She wants to learn and she does learn. She's a good teacher, too. She's also brutally frank, which occasionally shocks people. Her main job for the past few years has been as head of the Foster Care Committee here, to help women whose children are in foster care understand their responsibilities and rights and do whatever they can to keep their relationship with their children alive.

By the time Honey was twenty-five, she had three children, two girls and a boy. She had also racked up a series of misdemeanor charges for loitering, disturbing the peace and similar street offenses.

On the day that the crime which brought her to Bedford was committed she had spent the afternoon shopping with her three-year-old daughter, Shaniqua, and the man she was about to marry—a white man who had not fathered any of her children. It had been a tiring day for the child and she had been fussy all day. She had in her short life had one serious seizure and was taking prescribed medicine to control future ones.

That evening early, Honey, the baby, her fiancé, and another couple met for dinner in a local restaurant. "We got those looks when we walked in, you know what I mean, Jean. What's that nigger doing with a white man?" Service was slow, and the baby grew more and more restless. Twice, Honey took her to the bathroom. When the food finally came, Shaniqua had worked herself up into something bordering on a tantrum. Food ended up all over her, and for the third time Honey took her to the ladies room, this time to clean her up. No one else was there in the ladies room, but others in the restaurant said they could hear the child screaming and were sure "the mother was beating the child." Honey says Shaniqua fell and hit her head on the tile floor. She realized, quickly, the child was hurt, called her husband-to-be to help her, and they left to take the child to the hospital. Whether Shaniqua had had a seizure is unclear. Mother and child were both tired. It would have been better if they had taken the baby home and gone out to dinner later. But they didn't, so that's immaterial. Maybe Honey hit the child. My intuition says she did, but not repeatedly or there would have been signs. The child could easily have hit her head by accident.

Two weeks later Shaniqua died, cause of death a concussion. The couple who had been dining with them were subpoenaed as defense witnesses, but they disappeared and were never found. The woman had an outstanding warrant against her and didn't want to be found. The county pathologist testified that except for the blow on the head there were no signs that the child had ever been physically abused. There was no suggestion, or sign, that her two older children, who come to visit her and are in perfect health, were ever abused. Honey was indicted, went to trial, found guilty of murdering her child and sentenced to twenty-five years to life. She has served seven years.

They are victims, Maria and Honey, of their language, their origin, their color and the public's stereotypes about them. I believe in my heart, that with exactly the same evidence against her, and a decent lawyer, a white middle-class WASP in each case would have been acquitted. The American public, the justice system, Shaniqua, the children of both women are not served in any way by keeping them here. What more is there to say?

Twenty-two

"I know where my heart is. It went home and left me alone."

Where Katherine Davis devoted much of her energy to the study of prostitutes and efforts to save them from that life, today's superintendent of Bedford prison, Elaine Lord, has made the battered woman her main concern.

Her interest in the children of women prisoners is one of long standing, dating back well before she left Albany to come to Bedford. Her support of the prison's Children's Center from its inception is an important ingredient in its success. But now, her greatest energies are spent trying to make the public, and especially lawmakers, more aware of America's number one unreported crime—domestic violence.

Half a million instances of domestic abuse are reported every year, but some estimate that another five million go unreported. It may be abuse by a parent, a wife or husband, a lover or even a child. The battered women at Bedford are largely here because of a husband or lover, though the battering may have begun years before in their childhood home, where they learned to be victims.

Prompted by a meeting with members of the Inmate Liaison Committee, an inmate-elected group which, by law, must meet once a month with prison administration, Superintendent Lord and members of the New York State Division of Women listened to their request for some kind of prison program to help battered women. There are prison programs for alcoholics, drug addicts, those who have abused their children, those addicted to money, but the special problems of battered women were not being recognized, and their problems are unique.

It is one of the many ironies of this prison that many of the women with the longest terms are the least dangerous, and led the most useful lives before coming here. Asked what their police record before Bedford was, you may hear, "Well, I got a $40 speeding ticket on the Pennsylvania Turnpike." They were good daughters, good wives, good mothers and good citizens until the day or night the final straw of cruelty was piled on top of all the other straws, she broke and a husband or lover was killed. Depending upon the attitude of the judge and district attorney, they have been given anywhere from three to twenty-five years to life. Sonia's husband had a habit of breaking her arm. She finally killed him and got three years, was out in two. Garnell found her husband raping her daughter. She killed him and got eight and one-third to twenty-five. She's still here. Penny's husband was a policeman before he was fired from the force. She supported him for three more years while he threw dinner at her because he didn't like it and beat her brutally. She asked repeatedly for police protection from him, but you don't arrest an old buddy even if he did get fired for cause. She killed him and got eight and a third to twenty-five, too. Claudine's husband tried to kill her with acid and an ice pick. The top half of her body and face are horribly scarred and she must carry one arm up against her body, almost in a gesture of supplication. In the struggle, she threw some of the acid on him. He died of a heart attack. She has six to eighteen.

These are women who are victims as surely as anyone is a victim. And now they are twice victims. They all have children. Some have family nearby to take care of the children and bring them to see Mother whenever they can. Some of them have family on the other side of the world and, unless they turn the children over to foster care, will not see them again for many years. Some don't have the option. The husband's family fights for custody and promises, "You'll never see them again." Some of the women belong to Old World cultures where family vendettas are the norm and one death leads to many more. They live in terror.

Self-defense is not an accepted legal defense in New York State. Those women persuaded by counsel to plea-bargain are the wisest and end up with sentences of half or less than half of those who, naive, unschooled in the ways of justice, who felt what they did was ultimately done to save their own lives, went to trial and now pay for the privilege with fifteen or twenty-five years in prison.

The obvious question to ask, of course, is "Why did you put up with it? You're an idiot." The answers vary, but some always come to the top: "I loved him." "I was afraid of what he'd do to me if he caught me." "He kept promising he'd change." "I didn't have any other place for me and the children to go." "I was ashamed for my family and friends to know." "I was afraid it was all my fault so I lied about the bumps and bruises for years."

And there are other reasons, too. Many of these women were abused as children. It didn't start when they reached adulthood. It was their way of life. It had always been, they thought, the best they deserved. One of the young women here who killed her husband still has her first grade report card that says, "Evelyn has to learn to stand up for herself. The others pick on her because she lets them. They take her toys and push her out of line and she doesn't react. She has to learn to push back." She finally did at the cost of a man's life and fifteen years of hers, in here.

Superintendent Lord's idea was that while a prison program was needed, legislation was needed, too. And before legislators in Albany would take the problem seriously, they must be made aware of it and better informed about it. She sent around to every cell a brief questionnaire asking women if they had been battered as a child or adult, and whether they would consider discussing their experiences publicly. Many answered the questionnaire anonymously, but thirty signed their names and said yes to the last question. Lord invited all thirty to a meeting and described what she had in mind, a very public airing of their experiences in front of state representatives and senators, members of the New York State Division for Women, members of the press, social workers, judges and even some other inmates, to be chosen by them. It would not, she assured them, be easy to stand and publicly relive the night you killed a man you had loved, who had fathered your children. "I do not want to pressure anyone into doing it, except to tell you I think it could make a positive difference, if not for you, for your daughters." Some left in tears, knowing they couldn't possibly put themselves through that kind of emotional experience with the whole world watching. Twelve came back to the next meeting, and with that group Lord began a series of many meetings, some lasting late into the night, while the women talked and she listened. In time, they put their experiences on paper.

In September 1985, the large public gathering was held. The idea for the hearing was developed by Ronnie Eldridge, then director of the State Division for Women. Arrangements for the hearing and follow-up work were done with a great deal of support and assistance from others — notably Carol Lefcourt, counsel, and Linda Loffredo, program associate.

Each woman taking part was allowed to ask five inmates to come. I was asked and it proved to be one of the most highly emotionally charged days of my life, as the twelve women, standing one after the other alone, or with a friend beside her at the microphone and surrounded by hundreds of people, bared their souls. At the end of the meeting, which lasted all day, with lunch served in between, various suggestions were made as to legislation that could help stem the number of such tragedies. That police must now arrest the battering spouse when they are called is a beginning. Before this, the wife was asked if she wanted to press charges and usually said, "No," out of fear. Some suggested that the husband who beat his wife be required to move out and find other housing instead of wife and children having to leave as they presently do. Sister Elaine has opened five Providence Houses for battered women and their children, and they are always full. Others discussed a self-defense plea.

Everyone professed to have been deeply moved. Unfortunately, many went back to their offices and figured "something had been done." We had sat all day and listened to a few women tell sad stories—admittedly from their point of view. When the meeting was over, twelve women were left feeling very empty and wondering what the whole thing had been for. Superintendent Lord provided the support and understanding they badly needed. With their help, Lord wrote a proposal for a battered-women program, requesting funding for a therapist, counselor and social worker. So far, the therapist has materialized. It was during those weeks after the meeting that Lord again called the women together repeatedly to let them air their feelings and know that they had her support. One of them said to me, "To us Superintendent Lord has been a saint."

Some of the original group have finally gone home. Other new members have joined and with therapist Roberta Faulk they give workshops for battered women. The first meeting tells some of the myths and facts about family violence, in history, in mythology, in everyday life, in all cultures and societies. Wife battering is not a one-class crime. The second meeting is an effort to get new members to talk, something they are loathe to do until the "one-liners" begin. Older members place themselves in between new ones and start by giving some of the one-liners their husbands once used to put them down. "Who asked your opinion?" "Don't think, just get dinner." "What is this shit supposed to be." "Open your mouth you get a fist in it." "That's why we killed, Jean," one woman told me. "It wasn't the battered bodies. It was the battered soul. Being stripped inside." The ultimate purpose of the workshop is not to hate men, but to like themselves, and it has to begin with the things that made them feel inadequate.

Over the years, many jurors have listened to the cases of battered wives, usually quite unable to understand what kind of masochism would keep a woman in a home where she was mentally and physically abused. Experts call it the "battered woman syndrome." The cyclical repetition of violence causes some women to become so immobilized that "they sink into a state of psychological paralysis unable to take any action at all to change their situation." Psychiatrists call such conduct "learned helplessness."

That meeting two years ago at Bedford, and of course the efforts of a strong group of caring women—Elaine Lord, Ronnie Eldridge, Ruth Cassel, Carol Lefcourt, Linda Loffredo and others—played a vital role in the public's attitude toward Karen Straw and her recent acquittal. The purpose of their efforts is not to help women get away with murder, but to make us all aware of a serious national problem, and to find solutions to it before the final tragedy occurs. Statistically the child who grows up in a violent home has a far greater chance of becoming an abusive and violent parent or partner. And there is nothing more violent than poverty.

In a speech to a Conference on Domestic Violence, April 1986, Governor Cuomo said, "Studies of prisoners of war tell us that they ultimately become emotionally dependent on their jailers. What do we expect in situations where the jailer is the spouse or another loved one. Given this, the wonder is not that so many stay. The miracle is that some resist, separate and survive. But *some* are not enough."

In New Jersey, the courts have upheld the battered woman syndrome as "an appropriate subject for expert testimony." In Wyoming and Ohio, the supreme courts have ruled the other way. More teaching, a great deal more, is needed of the public, judges and lawmakers before some of the great injustices of this problem are corrected and avoided. Many of the battered women now in prison could be on probation in their own homes, working and supporting their children, financially, emotionally and educationally rather than locked into uselessness with their children serving a prison term with them.

Two years after the first public meeting, October 1987, a second meeting about domestic violence was held here at Bedford in the gym. Again, it included members of the State Division for Women, the Coalition on Domestic Violence, lawyers and women from the outside as well as inside with tragic tales of cruel abuse by husbands and lovers. Each inmate taking part was permitted to ask three inmates as part of the audience. Hence, I was again able to be there.

We were told that, according to the governor's Commission on Domestic Violence, "such violence occurs in approximately 50 percent of all families in the United States." While it happens in all socioeconomic brackets, the problems of poverty are inclined to exacerbate it. "Battering is the single major cause of injury to women. Up to four thousand women are beaten to death every year." Children often view mother's battering and grow up to be abusers or the abused. They accept it as a normal part of life.

"Battered women," we were told, "come to live a hostage existence. They identify with aggression, develop a pathological dependence on their battering partners . . . though they believe they and their children are at life-risk."

In spite of the work still to be done, there has been, in part due to the work being done at Bedford, some progress in making the country, and especially New York courts, aware of the enormity of the problem and some of the steps to be taken to ameliorate it. There are more homes now opened for battered women and their children, so they have "somewhere to go" when life becomes intolerable at home. Juries are beginning to accept the fact that some women who finally become violent toward their spouses do so because it becomes the only way to save themselves and their children. Karen Straw, who was acquitted of murdering her husband, was here, as was her lawyer, Mr. Michael Dowd. She is a very pretty, very private woman who obviously asks little more of life now than to be left alone to raise her children. The public appearance was difficult for her, and she obviously did it only as a symbol. Sadly the day after her appearance here she entered a mental hospital. Recovery from all she has experienced will probably be long and painful. For women already in here for ten years or twenty-five years to life for the same charge, it comes too late to save them.

Many of the women, like Karen Straw, had sought police protection, repeatedly, and been in and out of the hospital, repeatedly, with serious injuries. Among those who spoke briefly was a twenty-seven-year-old woman who had moved here from Yugoslavia with her husband and two sons, hoping to make a new start. His abuse of her continued and after he had dangled her by her heels out the fifth floor window, she killed him. She is here in Bedford for twelve years as part of her punishment. The worst part is that her husband's family have taken her sons and promised her she will never see them again.

The program ended on a highly emotional level with the entire audience locking hands, moving out into a single circle and singing "We Shall Overcome." When the music was over, and everyone's consciousness had been raised, and every woman had been assured repeatedly that she matters, and that a positive self-image is a very important thing to have, a C.O. announced, "No inmate is to leave the gym without being strip-searched." We were lined up at the door to the shower room and waited in line to be led into a cubicle to be stripped to the buff, "squat and cough," hands through the hair, shoes tapped on the side of a bench to make sure that none of the media or representatives from the governor's office had brought us in contraband. It seemed to me a good day to take a big chance and let us leave the room like women, instead of cattle.

There is still no legislation in the offing in New York to make better use of these women through one of many alternatives to prison, some way by which they can be with their children and earn their daily bread, as many did before they came here.

A lifetime of work by Katherine Davis hasn't stopped prostitution, hasn't legalized prostitution, hasn't stopped justice from wringing fines out of hookers and then sending them back to the street, hasn't begun to punish pimps as they should be punished, and still lets the customer walk away free *as air* to buy her services again another day. Whether Superintendent Lord's work will have a more lasting effect I don't know. I can only hope for the women and children involved, and the innocent needy citizens who are short-changed while New York pours its treasure into prisons and jails which compel useful, nondangerous women to be useless and indigent, that something better will be done, and soon.

Twenty-three

A sober view of man requires a modest definition of progress.

JAMES Q. WILSON

Physically, prisoners are better treated today than when Mr. Cromwell sold his farm to New York State for a reformatory. We are not beaten or whipped. We are not chained to the walls, and fed bread and water, nor do we have our faces dipped into pans of cold water as "treatment" to calm us down. Some may be chained to their beds if they have to go to the hospital, a practice that should have stopped before it started and which I am grateful was not inflicted upon me. The recent building of 200 cubicles as "regular housing" makes me very nervous, knowing I could be moved to one of them at any time and live out my life with all the privacy of an aardvark at the Bronx Zoo, and less fresh air.

Keep in mind that I can speak only of Bedford prison. The horrors of the two top, top federal security prisons, at Marion, Illinois, for men, and Lexington, Kentucky, for women, have lockdowns 23½ hours per day, complete silence, limited books and visits, no useful tasks to do and what have been called "sophisticated new techniques of behavior modification." The Lexington unit is all underground and holds only sixteen women. It will soon be replaced by a larger facility for 200 in Florida. In the meantime, some searches of females there are carried on by males, the women's showers have no curtains and are observed by male and female guards. Visits at Marion are through heavy Plexiglas, by phone. At Lexington, only one woman a day may have a visit.

By and large, it is only our minds that are played with here, and I don't believe that it is the policy so much as the practice of a few underlings. In its concerns and policy toward children and families of inmates, Bedford today shines bright. The visiting room is open seven days a week — 8:30 A.M. to 3:30 P.M. — and so is the Children's Center. Weekends are very crowded, weekdays are not. Once a month there is a free upstate bus for visitors that starts in Buffalo, stopping at Syracuse, Rochester and Albany, and goes all night to reach Bedford by 11:00 A.M., and then goes back the same day. It is paid for by the state. The Children's Center at the far end of the visiting room has one of the most active programs of any prison in the country to help the children of inmates.

There are four free buses per month from New York City. They are paid for by the Children's Center. The state pays for buses only if the prisons they go to are more than fifty miles from the bus's place of origin.

The uprising at Attica sparked the moves to increase visiting and writing privileges. Thomas A. Coughlin III, Commissioner of the New York State Department of Corrections, is a strong supporter of family visiting. He looks upon it, wisely, as a right, not a privilege. Many states still do not. A task force appointed by Coughlin produced a report in May 1984 saying, "Any effort that may contribute to the adoption of non-criminal behavior . . . by inmates following their release

266

from prison, must be viewed as being a potentially vital importance. . . . A critical component of this effort is a program that places emphasis upon healthy family functioning." There has been a growing awareness by prisons all over the country of the importance of family relationships and the role they play in avoiding recidivism. Statistically, the inmate who goes out to a supportive family has a far better chance of staying out. The married man or woman has a better chance still.

Bedford was among the first prisons — and is still one of comparatively few prisons — that permit family visits overnight, in fact for forty-six hours. The program began here in 1977 under a federal grant. By the end of 1980, 530 women who had participated in the program had been released. Four percent had returned with new charges or as parole violators, far less than the 36 percent statistic the state claims as its recidivism rate, and far, far less than the 70 percent others claim.

There are four trailers on the prison grounds, two with one bedroom and two with three bedrooms. Only legally married husbands may come, no common-law husbands. Here the trailers are largely used for mother, grandmother and child visits. The visits are healthy and humane and much looked forward to by the women and by the children as well. To have such a visit, the inmate must be cleared by this facility and by Albany.

The greatest problem for many women and families is getting together enough money to provide food for the family for forty-six hours. If the visit is permitted near the end of the month, it is not unusual for the food to run out before the visit is over. A nearby church sometimes comes to the rescue, and more than once Sister Elaine has rushed out to the grocery store, though there is nothing in her budget to cover such emergencies — no more than her budget covers the burial expenses of an indigent mother or father of an in-

267

mate or all the other tragic emergencies that are poverty's everyday fare.

Every woman I know here, without exception, praises the trailer visits and urges me to have one with my sons, David and Jim. I cannot and will not. The thought of them locked in here, at the mercy of the same arbitrary garbage that controls my life, is something I cannot accept. If they were younger and needed me in a different way, I'm sure I would feel differently. But as it is I am blessed in that they live nearby and can come frequently to visit. I don't want them ever to spend one night here.

Contact visits are permitted here. You may touch your visitors, sit near them. In the Children's Center, you may read to a child or rock her to sleep.

Eighty percent of American prisons now permit inmates to have contact visits. Only 25 percent of jails do. Basically, the difference between a jail and a prison is that sentences of less than a year are served in local jails, while terms of more than a year become the state's responsibility and are served in prison. But because so many people in jail cannot post bond for themselves, even a few hundred dollars, many spend more than a year in jail between waiting for trial and then serving their term.

There are still many jails in our country that forbid visits by children under the age of sixteen. If you're there for a year, the end of that year is when you'll next see your little children. Where contact is not permitted, you are separated from your visitor by glass or screen and conversations are carried on by phone. I have sat in such a booth in the jail at Valhalla. There are no words to describe how totally lost to the world it makes one feel. The conversation has the aura of a seance. It could terrify a child. It terrified me.

Some prisons permit infants to be brought into the visiting room but forbid bottles and diapers. Most prisons have no place for children to play while parents talk. They can crawl on the floor or sit and "keep quiet." They may not play with children visiting other inmates. "Cross visiting" is considered dangerous. Fewer than half of our women's prisons have visiting every day; in two states visiting is permitted every other Sunday for two hours. This makes for a visiting room so crowded there is not even a pretense at a private conversation. Even at Bedford, where visits are allowed every day, the weekends are sometimes so crowded the first in must leave before others can enter. One women's prison in the midwest allows each woman six hours of visiting per month, but for any visits on a holiday each hour counts as two! This sounds like something Louis XIV or Ivan the Terrible might have dreamed up. What right have we to do this to one another today? A judge's sentence says, "prison," it doesn't say "you may not see your children."

There is enough food for all at Bedford. It is, for the most part, good, as institutional food goes and the lack of it is never used as a punishment. A woman's prison in Florida has recently introduced a "bean loaf" with no seasoning or spices "to be fed to troublemakers until they grow so weary of it their behavior improves." I must confess, I reserve judgment on that. As long as it contains daily food value requirements and is fed to those who are capable of improving that's one thing. There are women in here who might starve to death before there was noticeable improvement. Second helpings are not permitted here, but first helpings are very generous. If you have a friend who works in the kitchen, of course, the sky's the limit. Family may bring an inmate two packages of food per month, adding up to no more than thirty-five pounds combined. There is a small kitchen with two burners on each floor for those who want to cook their own meals, and many do.

For me, one of the great blessings is that we can write as many letters as we wish. To write to people in other prisons requires permission from both superintendents and those letters may be read before they are mailed. Most outgoing mail is not read, but all is opened when it comes in to search for contraband.

We may receive books from friends and family and papers and magazines from publishers. Carmen, whose grandfather was president of Ecuador, whose father was chief justice of its Supreme Court, whose two sisters are lawyers, whose brother is an ambassador and who is herself a very nice, if not always wise, lady, was sent local papers weekly from a family friend, the Ecuadorian ambassador to the United States. When one of the package room C.O.s figured out they weren't coming from the paper's publisher, Carmen was no longer permitted to have them. And so much that matters goes unnoticed.

When books for inmates were first allowed into the prison they all had to come directly from the publisher, no books from home. This, of course, greatly restricted reading material since most poor people do not buy books from the publisher. They may buy them from a discount store, borrow them or find them on the subway, if they bother with them at all.

According to Jonathan Kozol in his book *Illiterate America*, our prison population represents the single largest concentration of adult illiterates in the country. Prison is hardly the place, therefore, to make a book hard to get. Unfortunately, there are still prisons in America today, in New York State, where inmates may have no more than two books in their cells at one time, and one of those must be the Bible, whether they want to read it or not.

A year ago, the New York Department of Corrections tried to resurrect, at Bedford, the old rule that books could come only from the publisher, in order, it said, to save the C.O.s the trouble of having to flip through the book pages to see if there is contraband hidden there. This for a few weeks took precedence over the importance of furthering literacy among people who, for society's sake as well as their own, should be encouraged to read. Worst of all, the ruling was interpreted by a C.O. in the package room as open season on anything printed. She began to refuse to give me even new books because, "You gots too many books." While I stood there she went back through the list of all the books I had signed for—in seven years, a great many. "But I don't have all those," I explained. "When I finish reading them I give most of them away." "It don't say you give 'em away on this paper," she said. For two weeks I wasn't even permitted to have a senior thesis a young friend from Bryn Mawr had sent me, because, "It's not from a publisher." I fled in terror to Dr. Matsuzaka, a kind psychiatrist. "My God!" I cried. "What will I do if they take away books?" The ruling has been withdrawn, I'm grateful to say, and we may now receive books from family and friends as well as publishers.

In addition to books sent to individuals there is a good prison library here. I have reason to believe it is one of the best prison libraries in the country, thanks to a fine librarian, generous neighborhood libraries and friends, as well as publishers and authors. We also have a Law Library, and a library for the children in our Children's Center. Generous gifts keep it fresh and interesting and make it possible for us to give many books to the children to take home.

Some good things happen here, no question. A woman can go from adult basic education to a bachelor's degree, if she chooses to. She can take parenting courses—if she chooses to. She can learn English if she chooses to. Until 1978 it was against the prison rules to speak Spanish here. If you were heard, you got a charge sheet. Then a busload of Hispanics and activists picketed the facility and the rule changed. Now, if you stay here for fifteen years you don't have to make any attempt to learn English, even if you're an American citizen. One thing you can't learn in here, even if you choose to, is how to get to work on time. Responsibility and punctuality are not hot ticket items in prison and neither is logic. I think I miss the latter most of all. The absence of it can wear away the brain. It brings out the worst in me.

In this prison, C.O.s harass the inmates, and the inmates harass the C.O.s. I've seen a C.O. work laboriously for two hours writing charge sheets for women who didn't jump fast enough for him. Having finished the job, he chose, unwisely, to go to the bathroom. As soon as he closed the bathroom door a woman tiptoed to the bubble, grabbed the charge sheets, tore them and flushed them down the nearest toilet. The confused C.O. spent the next two hours looking for them. It's boarding-school stuff played with Keystone Kops.

The ubiquitous memos that actually run the place are not fun and games. Here are the rules about the phone room on my cell block in the past seven months:

The phone room will be unlocked at 9:30 A.M.
The phone room will be unlocked at 8:00 A.M.
The phone room will be unlocked at 8:00 A.M., but any woman not leaving the floor at 7:45 A.M. will be locked in her cell until 11:30 A.M.
Until 11:30 A.M., a woman must sign up for the phone, and then will be allowed to use it, at the discretion of the C.O.

Each new memo was posted. Each one causing the usual confusion and anger.

Somehow, in the flood of paper, the reason for opening the door at 8:00 A.M. has been lost. Cause and effect, problem and solution are no longer related. At 11:30 A.M. when everyone returns to the cell block to get ready for lunch, sixty women can now race for the phone.

Each example of harassment is petty. Piled one on top of another they can become what nervous breakdowns are made of, an obsession, the last miserable straw. Take the corridor between the School Building and Traffic. Whether what happened there was motivated by stupidity or unvarnished nastiness, I don't know. I work five mornings a week in the Children's Center office, which is in the School Building. I often have need, many inmates do, to walk to the area called Traffic, in a nearby building. The Traffic area leads to the visiting room, package room, counselors' offices and the Administration Building.

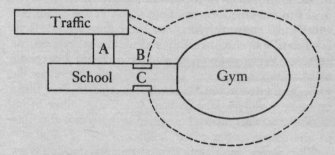

The two buildings are connected by an enclosed corridor (A), which has been used by both staff and inmates every day for the seven and a half years I have been here and long before that. Suddenly, the Security Department decided that only staff are now to use the corridor. All inmates must go outside to walk between the buildings. For the first two months, we were allowed the special privilege of using exit B to make the trip. After two months of exit B, I knocked at that door one cold afternoon only to be told by the C.O. on duty,

273

"That's the last time I open this door. From now on you only use that door," pointing to exit C. "But why," I asked. His answer was the usual Bedford non sequitur, since opening door C for me and all inmates requires more walking and more work for him than door B. "I'm not here to serve you," he answered. "That raises an interesting question," I said. "What are you here for?" He didn't tell me.

After four months, the system gradually died out, not because someone said, "This is outrageous, it must stop at once." It simply petered away because the game stopped being fun and became a mere inconvenience. The regular C.O. had known at once it made no sense and stopped as soon as he could without disobeying orders from on high. But different C.O.s move in and out of areas with no idea of what the recent memo says or preferring their own rules to facility rules.

Try to imagine for a moment that you are an inmate who is told constantly that she must improve her "self-image" if she is to prepare herself to make it on the outside. What possible constructive result can come from telling her daily, "You don't walk where people walk. Outside for you." How does this correct anything or make society safer? In fact, it left a number of inmates to wander around outside, with no one checking to see if they ever reached Traffic.

The same department has recently added new touches to the hardware that must be worn when one is taken outside to court or to the hospital. No longer are handcuffs sufficient. One must wear handcuffs with a black box attached in between, so the hands cannot move at all, and the wrists can be rubbed raw. The cuffs are then attached to chains around the waist and ankles. Try these on for size when you're nine months pregnant. They tell me I need a stress test for which I go to the outside hospital. Getting there is the stress test. Thinking about getting there is the stress test. The solution is simple. I don't go.

Wednesday morning is the time the nursery mothers and their babies are scheduled to come to the Children's Center. They are welcome other days as well, but this is the day that special activities are planned for them, and a small group of them meet with me there for a Parenting Class. It has taken six weeks of false starts to get the new class going. If the day wasn't wrong, the hour was wrong, if the class was held where the mothers were, I wasn't allowed to be there; if the class was held where I was, the mothers weren't allowed to be there. It is the sixth class I have taught and each time we go through the same frustrations and waste of time, as though Security were considering all its dangerous possibilities for the first time, and the safety of the modern world were at stake.

The mothers and babies arrived last Wednesday morning with their C.O. escorts as always, ready to go through one last door to the Children's Center. The C.O. on duty, whose job it is to pat-frisk inmates and then open the door for them, decided that pat-frisking the mothers and their babies and opening the door was simply too much work for her. "Go back to your floor," she ordered them. "I'm not opening the door." The women balked and refused. "This is where we're supposed to be." "I'm giving you a direct order to turn around and get outta here. You refuse a direct order, you'll lose your babies." I heard her say it. When you refuse a direct order, you get a charge sheet and are locked, and it could mean having your baby sent out to family or foster care. The women were doing exactly what they were supposed to do, and a C.O. was threatening them with losing their children to others if they didn't immediately obey a rule she had just made up and which was at odds with a program approved by the prison's top administration. It took the intervention of a staff teacher, the interruption of an executive meeting

275

of the prison administration and the direct order of a deputy superintendent to get the door open. In the meantime everyone was angry and upset, nerves were on edge and some were actually frightened. While she was made to open the door, the C.O. managed to have the last word. When the mothers and babies left the area, she strip-searched each mother and child as slowly as she could. After an hour and a half of waiting to be searched and going through the search, the noon count was frozen so the babies could not go back to their floor for another forty minutes. "But the babies are missing their lunch," the mothers cried. "So what," the C.O. said. "I'm missin' mine too!" As an inmate I am required to call this woman a "Corrections Officer." You may call her what she is.

In a sense, one could say prison is the archetype of democracy gone mad. It is power in the hands of people ill-equipped to use it wisely. "Dressed" as Shakespeare wrote, "in a little brief authority, most ignorant of what they're most assured."

Sad to say, tragic to say, such shortsighted, and in my opinion counterproductive, treatment is quite in keeping with one of the most shocking Supreme Court decisions in recent years, one that I probably would not have noticed eight years ago or attached little importance to had I noticed it. In July 1984, the Supreme Court of the United States proclaimed, in a five to four decision, led by then Chief Justice Warren Burger, that no prisoner in the United States has "any right to any personal dignity." One can only be grateful that so few C.O.s read about or care about what the Supreme Court decides. Unfortunately many of them live by that decision even if they don't know that those on high have proclaimed it.

In the case that prompted the decision, a C.O. had entered a prisoner's cell in a state prison in Virginia and torn up the prisoner's legal papers, his wife's letters to him and his children's pictures. Every lower court which heard the prisoner's case held that inmates have a limited legal privacy interest which protects them against seizure of their personal belongings when there is no issue of prison security. Every lower federal court that considered the case determined that prison cells are protected to some extent by the Fourth Amendment's prohibition against illegal search and seizure. Mr. Burger and four others disagreed. But they didn't stop there. They determined that the Fourth Amendment does not protect prisoners at all, ever, "no matter how extreme the circumstances."

Judge Stevens felt so appalled by the decision that he chose to read his dissent aloud. "By telling prisoners," he wrote, "that no aspect of their individuality, from a photo of a child to a letter from a wife, is entitled to Constitutional protection, the Court breaks with the ethical tradition that I had thought was enshrined forever in our jurisprudence."

One must have experienced prison as an inmate to know into what kind of hands this power of destruction has been placed. The young C.O. who is presently pregnant with her third illegitimate baby, the woman who said I had stolen a "bushel of blueberries," the woman who goaded me daily to get me to hit her so she could scream "assault" and have me put in solitary, the male C.O.s who impregnate inmates, the female C.O. who gets so stoned on duty I have seen her struggle to unlock a door while pushing the key into the door two feet above where the lock was. Anyone of these and many more like them could walk into my cell as I sit here and tear up the pictures of my sons and the manuscript I am writing and anything else that strikes their fancy, and they can do so with the approval of the United States Supreme Court.

I have brought hundreds of young people to visit our Supreme Court, waited in long lines with them because I believed it was so important that they be touched by its history and know the role it plays in our lives. Obviously, I didn't know the role myself. I have sat with them in hushed awe while those nine very special people listened to a case being argued. I've kept an old copy of one of Justice Burger's graduation speeches in which he said every prisoner must be taught to read and write in English and master a marketable skill. I was impressed by that speech long before prison touched my own life. But now I must ask, "How do you teach anything to a human being whom you have stripped of 'all personal dignity'?" You have created a social, emotional and intellectual zombie.

As for the prisoner whose cell was trashed and who brought the case to court? In going through his cell, the C.O.s found a State pillowcase he had destroyed. He got a charge sheet.

Father Gorman said to me one day, "If the lives of many of these young women could be painted into a picture, the picture would be too ugly for our eyes to see." That doesn't relieve the women of the responsibility for their own actions, but it does suggest that all the good people should pause before throwing stones or before deciding who all the victims are.

Epilogue

Mac.
Yeah Dessa.
I'm goin take you out with me when I go.
How you goin do that?
I'll break you up in little atoms and molecules and take you outta here. And then I'll get you back together again . . . course, maybe I ain't gonna get you back together again, in which case you just gonna havta float around in the atmosphere.
I'll chance it, Dessa. I'll chance it.

Weeks have gone by since I began, many weeks. The sameness of prison life doesn't change — only the names of the women who hurt most this week.

Vickie died on a Thursday. She had had almost three weeks outside in a hospice, where her children and friends could be with her and she could be a mother and woman for a little while. Sherry and Kelly organized a service for her here at the prison. We held it in the gym because the floor of the chapel is falling in.

We sat in a semicircle, there were about one hundred of us, and Ceci sang, and a trio sang, and women went up one at a time, a little like a Quaker meeting and said what was in their hearts about Vickie. Kelly said, "For those of us who have 'hard time' like Vickie did, I'll always remember how they came into Vickie's room just before she went out and said to her, 'You understand, Miss Ardito, if you get better you've still got to come back and serve nine more years.' And Vickie said, 'I'll be glad to serve nine more years.' "

Sandy went up, too. She's dying of AIDS, but she wanted to say something special about Vickie. Sandy has been here at Bedford for eight and one half years. She admits, "There were four of us used to get heroin in and then share a needle. That was in '81, '82, '83. We'd never heard of AIDS then. We sure heard of it now."

Another woman remembered last Christmas when Vickie asked all the other fifty-nine women on her floor what they'd like most for Christmas. Then she found pictures of all the things in magazines, cut them out and put them in envelopes, with a ribbon, and Christmas afternoon she called them all together and gave each one her gift.

Ceci sang a gospel song by Andraé Crouch:

Tell them, even if they don't believe you
Tell them, even if they won't receive you
Just tell them for me
Please tell them for me
That I love them, and I came to let them know.

A big sign over the prison stage in back of where she stood says, "We women can make it on our own." For an hour, Vickie brought out the parts in all of us that make people beautiful.

Ceci will be out of here in a year and be paroled to Boston. She has no parents, no home to go back to, nothing but a beautiful voice. Someone should be out there waiting to give her an audition. One audition would do it.

Her family will bury Vickie in a place of the family's choosing. For women who die in prison with no one to claim their bodies there is an old graveyard in a small glen, surrounded by a ring of trees, across the street from Bedford, on what is now Taconic's property. There are babies buried there as well as women. Not all the graves have names, but all of them have numbers. If I am left here to die, I want to be buried there.

Some inmates jumped Loretta and would have killed her if they hadn't been dragged off of her. She was trying to sign up for a TV program she wanted to see, but the C.O. said the sign-up book didn't work and to throw it away. When she refused, the fight started. A sign-up system of course could work, and is the only equitable way for sixty women to share one TV. But it would entail a little time and effort for a C.O., so it has been discontinued.

Loretta went to the prison hospital with cracked ribs, a concussion, purple eyes—one eye seriously damaged, puffed and closed—and a wicked contusion on her back where a woman beat her with a metal cart. After she had fallen to the floor she was kicked in the head twice, while I stood there, ineffectually crying, "Stop it! Stop it!" and a friend cried, "Jean, get the hell outta there or I'll have to get in to save you." Finally Loretta went into a seizure, was incontinent and lay there on the floor for about fifteen minutes until a nurse came. The C.O.s and inmates just stood around and stared.

I went to visit her three days later. She was lying in bed in the same dirty blouse she was wearing the night she was beaten. "The prison hospital does not stock clean nightgowns or pajamas," I was told.

There were five women involved in the attack, but only one was punished. She was given twenty days in lock, which is the equivalent of a slap on the wrist for felonious assault. The others were given no punishment because the C.O. "wrote their charge sheets wrong." Three weeks later, the woman who kicked Loretta in the head was given parole. Loretta was given a charge sheet, stamped Superintendent Hearing, for starting the argument about the TV and refusing a direct order to throw the sign-up sheet away. This is known as the "corrections system." I think it is also referred to by some as "justice."

The AIDS crisis has left Bedford's medical department as unprepared for the new demands put upon it as are medical departments all over the country, and especially in New York City. To date, I know of fifteen women who have died of it who spent much of their illness time in Bedford's IPC (In Patient Care unit). I'm told more than forty other women here are infected with the AIDS virus. Since so many of the women lived a life of prostitution and IV drug use before coming here, one would expect the number to be larger. It probably is.

A recent court-ordered report on the medical care at Bedford Hills concluded that the facility was "woefully unequipped" to handle the number of cases here and called for sweeping changes. A state-sponsored study commissioned by the Department of Correctional Services was quite different and praised improvements in facility medical care. Superintendent Lord says one of the greatest problems is that women who believe they have AIDS won't come forward and say so. They are afraid of being ostracized and, for many, the friends they have in here are all they have. Testing is not mandatory, which is just as well. Since there is no cure, testing would create far more problems than it would solve.

Out of the tragedies and fear that AIDS has brought, one positive thing has evolved. Five inmates — Mo, Kathy, Rosie, TJ and Diane — have taken the initiative, with administrative approval, to establish the ACE program (AIDS Counseling and Education program). They have arranged for knowledgeable staff members from Montefiore Hospital to give them a course in AIDS counseling and have established a buddy system for women with AIDS or ARC, so no one will be left to suffer friendless and alone. They are also working to make connections with outside groups so there will be help for women who leave here.

While the ACE group has grown, another group of inmate volunteers, led by Sheila and Kelly, have taken it upon themselves to "adopt" the women in ICP and help them revamp their cells, from dark, dank, cockroach-infested areas, to freshly painted, polished, livable areas they are now proud of. It has made a visible difference in the self-esteem of both the helpers and the helped. With all the ugliness, there are still compassion and goodness here in those whom the world would call wicked.

Rosie keeps having her seizures and slipping back into childhood. I lured her back into her cell and into bed with a chocolate mint one morning. She stuffed it into her mouth with both hands, nodded toward me and said to the C.O., "She's nice. She's my social worker."

Ducky's husband has become a Moslem since she came to prison and has written to tell her he has chosen a second wife. "She is willing to accept you," he writes, "why can't you accept her?" Ducky says, "I don't think I can ever accept her, but if I don't I'll lose him." If only we could be objective about ourselves instead of everyone else.

Tina says she still feels herself getting very depressed about her baby's death, a frightening feeling, one more dark tunnel in a surfeit of tunnels, and maybe this will be the one she can't find her way out of. I know what she means. The signs of depression terrify me. Will I be able to shake it off this time or will it bury me? "I keep real busy, Jean. I try to keep real busy." "I know, Tina," I say. "So do I."

Cora is now in the psychiatric ward of Kings County Hospital. Sister Elaine took her there after giving her a try at Providence House IV, a halfway house for paroled women. It was more freedom than Cora could handle. In time she will go into a special home, but its waiting list is long. In the meantime she calls Sister almost every day, collect, to tell her "thank you for bringing me here." Had she gone to the women's shelter the parole officer offered her, she would probably be dead by now or back in prison with a new offense. I think the bingo nights she spent at Bedford were some of the happiest evenings of her life. It is ironic that I waited until I came to this evil place to fall down on my knees and thank God for the life I have lived.

Jennifer, an emotional, naive young woman was given sixty days in solitary for writing "properganda material." She was housed in the new dormitory wing with cubicles instead of cells, next to a woman with an advanced case of AIDS. She thought the woman was too ill to be out of the hospital and wasn't getting proper care. It was a story one reads so often today, both in and out of prison, about something so big and so frightening none of us yet has good answers.

In a frenzy of emotion and frustration, Jennifer sat up one night pouring out her concern over a long yellow pad and ending with the cry, "something must be done." She showed me what she had written; it was earnest and redundant and nothing we hadn't already thought, or said, or read about in the newspapers.

She made ten copies of the writing, and put them in envelopes to mail to family, friends and the media. The envelopes were lying on her bed when two C.O.s entered her cubicle for a search. They took the envelopes with them when they left, leaving her with a receipt saying the ten "packets" were "properganda" material, as opposed to "improperganda," which I can only suppose is even worse.

It wasn't an accidental error. It was spelled improperly three times by the C.O. and twice by the person who presided at the Superintendent's Hearing, a procedure used only for the most serious breaches of rules in here. The latter added she had "addmitted to writting the said properganda." She was found guilty of 104.12: "Inmates shall not organize any action which may be detrimental to the order of the facility." She hadn't organized any action at all.

"The materials," she was told, "could have excited other inmates and led to a serious breakdown of security within the institution." I've heard countless numbers of AIDS stories in here, far hairier than Jennifer's. Nonetheless, for this breach of security she was given sixty days in lock, taken to SHU, relieved of all her clothing, given a flannel wrapper and locked. A few hours later, around midnight, she was unlocked, given back her clothes and told that her punishment was canceled. A few days later, she received a copy of a letter, which was also sent to her lawyer and to Linda Singer, the Special Master appointed by the courts to oversee breaches of the law in punishing inmates at Bedford Hills. It was signed by a Deputy Superintendent who said the reason for the reversal was that during the taping of the inmate's testimony there was a break in the tape. How refreshing it would be if just once they'd level and say "we blew it." Their legal bills would probably be much lower. The letters have never been returned.

A day later, a high staff person drew Jennifer aside and asked her confidentially, "Say, tell me, did you write anything about me in that letter?" "No I didn't," she answered, "but I have to tell you this has been a very frightening experience." "Good!" he answered. "Maybe now you'll keep your pen in your pocket."

It wasn't said to me, but for me it was the throwing down of the gauntlet. I will think of those words every time I take my pen from my pocket and write about this place.

Susie got a charge sheet when a small marigold plant she had grown from a cutting was seized. The charge sheet read, "Appears to be marijuana."

I carried a pint of blueberries from the Children's Center into the traffic area, to use as a bingo prize and got a charge sheet for "stealing a bushel of blueberries."

The superintendent of a prison cannot guide the hands and mouths of each of her staff members. I try to imagine running anything where most of the employees have great power over the lives of others and the public purse as well, but the person at the top cannot hire or fire them. It is a difficult and unenviable position.

But some of the foolishness comes down from on high, too. Per a recent memo: Women who live in the dormitory area where there are not individual sinks and toilets may not go to the toilet during the four daily counts, no matter how long they take.

If someone is kind enough to send you stationery and put stamps on the envelopes, you can have the paper but not the envelopes. If you want to use them you must make an appointment each time with your counselor, bring your letter down, he will stuff the envelope, seal it and mail it. God knows why. You can go to the commissary and buy stamps, but you can't be given them.

Christmas is coming as I bring this to a close. We've gathered lovely gifts from kind friends and caring people far and near so that the mothers can pick out two gifts for each of their children and grandchildren, wrap them and have them in the Children's Center when the children come. It would touch you to know how many women, given the opportunity to wrap the gifts themselves, tell you, "I don't know how. I never wrapped a gift before." In the *favella* of Rio perhaps, in the peasant villages of Siberia maybe, but here, in the land of opportunity and plenty?

Glenua won't be picking up Christmas gifts for her children this year. "They're with my sister up in Canada. They haven't got the money to come." Dorothy will be seeing her eight-year-old son for the first time in more than a year. He was hit by a car and has been in a body cast for months. She is patient and philosophical. "Our kids play in the streets, Jean. You play in the streets, you get hit by a car."

Auriole came in to pick out gifts for her ten-year-old son. When I questioned whether her choices were appropriate for a ten-year-old boy, she told me, "He was hit by a car, Jean. There's brain damage. It's been two years and he's just beginning to come back." Auriole herself was limping. She had spent the day before going in and out of seizures and had thrown her back painfully out of alignment. Her mother has her son. Her sister who has three little children has just been diagnosed as having cancer. "And so it goes," as the lady says.

A popular refrain—when people, both inside and outside of prison, discuss prisoners and how to prepare them to lead a decent life when they leave prison—goes like this, "We must help them improve their self-image. They hate themselves so much they have stopped caring how they act." Having thus pontificated, they then proceed to bend, fold, staple, crush and mutilate every bit of self-image they can attach their memos to. Prisons are run by memos, little pious pieces of paper that we have learned to duplicate in senseless numbers and just as quickly lose, so there are always at least two points of view as to what the lost memo said. Sometimes they have the mark of the Delphic Oracle upon them, so ambiguous you can take your choice of meanings. These are especially useful to people who don't want to be blamed for anything, of which there are a great many in any business I suppose, and make no mistake about it: Prisons, whatever else they may be, are big business.

There are good things that happen here, things that warm the heart. We are truly blessed that the administration cares and permits us the unique privilege of providing presents for inmate children. Kathy, oh so earnest Kathy, put on a play one morning last week, written by the beginning readers she is working with to bring out of the dark. Superintendent Lord and two of her deputies came to see it, and that matters very much.

Yet with all the basic decency, the good things that place this prison in the forefront of every women's prison in America, there's always the niggling new memo to pull back the forward push.

"There is entirely *too* much fimilarity in this prison between inmates and staff," (emphasis and spelling theirs) a new memo reads. Henceforward, no inmate is ever to call a staff person by first name. They must be addressed as Ms., Mrs., or Mr., or by their title, 'Teacher O'Rourke,' not Pat, whom some of us have known and worked with and loved for years.

"Starting Monday inmates may not wear any jewelry in the visiting room." (You can still wear a religious medal, but sooner or later someone will decide that's unconstitutional. If I worship mammon may I still wear my pearls?)

Tomorrow is another day in the history of Bedford Hills Correctional Facility, and the memos, those silly, soul-shattering, stomach-churning memos, will probably never stop coming. I think what frightens me most about them is that I know I was once capable of writing such stuff myself, unable to see the things that mattered most, all in the name of honorable intentions and "doing the right thing."

The justice system and the correctional system, as I have experienced them, fear truth and common sense like the Wicked Witch of the West feared water. So much of what they decree and condone and profess to believe melts away with a simple application of truth or common sense or compassion. Heaven knows there are plenty of women here who know little about compassion or decency toward others. But they'll never learn about it unless society shows them some first. If the public is wise, it will have sent us here to learn useful lessons, not to be reminded in every conceivable way that we are the human refuse of these teeming shores. If the public is wise, the children of inmates who have never hurt others but have only been hurt will be gathered up into our loving concern and taught compassion and the will to learn while there is still time to save them from these hallowed halls.

The women's behavior has its strident and violent days and occasional quiet days, too. From time to time I think of Katherine Davis's words, "They are not *like* bad girls. They *are* bad girls. They are strong individualists. So are children. Social consciousness is asleep in the criminal as it is in the child. In both it must be awakened, and after it is awakened, trained."

The only constant here is the sound of a C.O.s voice calling "Ladies, ladies." If Dodie and her butch are stretched out on the couch in the rec making love, if Cupcake is screaming out the window to her lover, Monique has just suggested to the C.O. that he's a "Dumb nigger. Don't know where your ass is at," and the Greek chorus in the background is chanting the Bedford mantra, "Fuck dat shit, fuck dat shit, fuck dat shit," when a C.O. is finally moved to say something, you can bank on it, you can run for Congress on it, he'll call out "Ladies, ladies."

We built a wall
To separate dangerous from dangered
Like in from out
With a one-way door
Like life to death
With two sides
Like left to right
One with guards, the other guarded
Like good to bad
If we're so organized
Where did we go wrong?

Jonathan Lacey

References
and Bibliography

Adler, Freda. *Sisters in Crime: The Rise of the New Female Criminal*. New York: McGraw-Hill, 1976.

Austin, Roy. "Women's Liberation and Increases in Minor, Major and Occupational Offenses." *Criminology*, vol. 2, Nov. 1982.

Barry, Ellen. "Quality of Prenatal Care for Incarcerated Women Challenged." *Youth Law News*, Nov/Dec. 1985.

Baunach, Phyllis. "Mothering from Behind Prison Walls." Paper presented at annual meeting of the American Society of Criminology, Nov. 1979.

———. "You Can't Be a Mother and Be in Prison." Draft of a study, 1982.

Bloom, Benjamin. *Stability and Change in Human Characteristics*. New York: John Wiley & Sons, 1964.

Bowlby, John. "Attachment and Loss: Retrospect and Prospect." *American Journal of Orthopsychiatry*, Oct. 1982.

Bruner, J. S., et al. *Studies in Cognitive Growth: A Collaboration at the Center for Cognitive Studies*. New York: John Wiley & Sons, 1966.

Burkhart, Kathryn. *Women in Prison*. Garden City,

N.Y.: Doubleday & Co., 1973.

Carey, Eve, and Kathleen Peratis. *Women and the Law*. New York: National Textbook Co., with the ACLU, 1984.

Children's Defense Fund. "Black and White Children in America: Key Facts." Washington, D.C., 1985.

Clausmeyer, Ann. "Westfield: Women's Prison with a Touch of Humanity." *Reporter Dispatch,* Sept. 30, Oct. 1 & 2, 1965.

Committee on Domestic Violence and Incarcerated Women. "Battered Women and Criminal Justice," June 1987.

Comptroller General of the United States, Report to Congress. "Women in Prison: Inequitable Treatment Requires Action."

Correctional Association of New York. "Attica 1982: An Analysis of Conditions in New York State Prisons." Report, Sept. 1982.

Crime and Social Associates, *Punishment and Penal Discipline,* 1982.

Crittendon, Ann. "New Insights into Infancy." *New York Times,* Nov. 13, 1983.

Cummings, Judith. "For Black Families the Odds Are Formidable." *New York Times,* Dec. 1983.

Davis, Katherine B. *Factors in the Sex Life of Twenty-two Hundred Women*. Salem, N.H.: Ayer Co., 1972.

———. "A Study of Prostitutes Committed from New York City to the State Reformatory for Women at Bedford Hills." 1912.

Delinger, David. "Playing with Prisoners Minds." *Fellowship,* vol. 54, March 1988.

Dillard, J. L. *Black English: Its History and Usage in the United States*. New York: Random House,

1972.

Engle, Kathleen, and Stanley Rothman. "Prison Violence and the Paradox of Reform." *The Public Interest,* Fall 1983.

Episcopal Mission Society in the Diocese of New York, with the New York State Department of Correction. *Mothers and Babies at Westfield State Farm,* Jan. 1965.

Feinman, Clarice C. *An Historical Overview of the Treatment of Incarcerated Women: Myths and Realities of Rehabilitation,* 1977.

———. "Sex Role Stereotypes and Justice for Women." *Crime and Delinquency,* Jan. 1979.

———. *Women in the Criminal Justice System.* New York: Praeger, 1980.

Forer, Judge Lois G. *Criminals and Victims.* New York and London: Norton & Co., 1980.

Fox, James G. "Women's Prison Policy, Prisoner Activism, and the Impact of the Contemporary Feminist Movement: A Case Study."

Fraiberg, Selma. *Every Child's Birthright.* New York: Basic Books, 1977.

Freedman, Estelle B. *Their Sisters' Keepers: Women's Prison Reform in America 1830-1930.* Ann Arbor: University of Michigan Press, 1981.

Friedrich, Otto. "What Do Babies Know?" *Time* magazine, Aug. 15, 1983.

Gamer, E., and A. Schrader. "Children of Incarcerated Parents: Problems and Interventions." In *Management of Behavior Associated with Marital Discord.*

Gardner, John. *Excellence: Can We Be Equal and Excellent Too?* New York: Norton & Co., 1984.

Genevie, Louis, Ph.D., and Eva Margolis. *The Motherhood Report.* New York: Macmillan, 1987.

General Accounting Office of the United States. "Female Offenders: Who They Are and What Are the Problems Confronting Them," Aug. 1979.

Georgia Department of Offender Rehabilitation. "Female Offenders in the Eighties."

Glick, R., and V. Neto. *National Study of Women's Correctional Programs*. Published by the National Institute of Law Enforcement and Criminal Justice, Law Enforcement Assistance Administration, United States Department of Justice, 1977.

Goodlad, John. *A Place Called School*. New York: McGraw-Hill, 1983.

Grossman, Judy. "Family History of Selected Female 1987 Commitments." State of New York Department of Correctional Services, Feb. 1982.

Gubar, Susan, and Ann Hedin. "A Jury of Our Peers: Teaching and Learning in the Indiana Women's Prison." *College English*, Dec. 1981.

Guttmacher Institute. "Teenage Pregnancy: The Problem That Hasn't Gone Away."

Haiman, Franklin S., ed. *Woman and the Law*. National Textbook Co., with American Civil Liberties Union, 1984.

Hale, Janice. *Black Children: Their Roots, Culture and Learning Styles*. Provo, Utah: Brigham Young University Press, 1982.

———. "De-Mythicizing the Education of Black Children." In *Educating Blacks*.

Haley, Kathleen. "Mothers Behind Bars." *New England Journal of Prison Law*, vol. 4, 1977.

Harlow, H. F. "The Nature of Law." *American Psychologist*, 1958.

Harper's magazine. "Moving Up at Last: Being

Black in America." *Forum,* Feb. 1987.

Harrington, Michael. *The New American Poverty.* New York: Holt, Rinehart & Winston, 1984.

Harvard Medical School. "Psychiatric Implications of Child Neglect." Mental Health Letter, Dec. 1986.

Heidensohn, Frances. *Women and Crime: The Life of the Female Offender.* New York: New York University Press, 1983.

Hendrix, Omar. "A Study in Neglect: A Report on Women Prisoners," 1972.

Holt, Karen. "Nine Months to Life: The Law and the Pregnant Inmate." *Journal of Family Law,* vol. 20, no. 3, 1982.

Holt, N., and D. Miller. "Explorations in Inmate-Family Relationships." State of California Research Division, Department of Corrections. Report No. 46.

Honig, Bill. *Last Chance for Our Children: How You Can Help Save Our Schools.* Reading, Mass.: Addison-Wesley, 1985.

Ibuka, Masuru. *Kindergarten Is Too Late.* New York: Simon & Schuster, 1977.

James, Jennifer. *The Prostitute as Victim: Criminal Justice System and Women.* New York: Clark Boardman Co. Ltd., 1982.

Jensen, Arthur. *Bias in Mental Testing.* New York: Macmillan, 1980.

Kagan, Jerome. *The Nature of the Child.* New York: Basic Books, 1984.

Kohl, Herbert. *Basic Skills.* Boston: Little, Brown, 1982.

Kozol, Jonathan. *The Night Is Dark and I Am Far from Home.* New York: Continuum, 1984.

Krisberg, Barry, and James Austin. "The Unmet

Promise of Alternatives to Incarceration." San Francisco: National Council on Crime and Delinquency Research Center, 1982.

Lane, Mary. Education for Parenting. Washington, D. C.: National Association for the Education of Young Children, 1975.

Large, Jean. "A Man's Job." *University of Chicago Magazine,* Jan. 1934.

Locke, Jill, and Margaret Kimmel. "Children of the Information Age: Changes and Challenges." *Library Trends,* Winter 1987.

Lord, Elaine A. "Adjustment Patterns of Women Inmates," 1980.

McDermott, Joan, ed. "Female Offenders in New York State." *New York State Division of Criminal Justice Services,* Nov. 1985.

McGowan, Brenda, and Karen Blumenthal. *Why Punish the Children?* San Francisco: National Council on Crime and Delinquency, 1978.

Martin, Del. "Battered Women; Society's Problem." In *The Criminal Justice Systems and Women.* New York: Clark Boardman Co. Ltd., 1982.

Martin, Suzanne. "The Children of Women in Prison." In *A Case Study of New Jersey's Correctional Institution for Women.* Woodrow Wilson School of Public Affairs, 1974.

Mednick, Sarnoff. "Crime in the Family Tree." *Psychology Today,* March 1985.

Miller, Alice. *Prisoners of Childhood.* New York: Basic Books, 1981.

Moynihan, Daniel P. *Family & Nation: The Godkin Lectures, Harvard University.* San Diego: Harcourt Brace Jovanovich, 1986.

———. "The Negro Family: The Case for National Action." Washington, D.C.: Government Printing Office, 1965.

Murray, Charles. *Losing Ground, American Social Policy 1950-1980*. New York: Basic Books, 1984.

National Institute of Justice. "Relationship of Adult Criminal to Juvenile Delinquency."

Nebitt, Charlotte. "Female Offenders: A Changing Population." *Corrections Today,* Feb. 1986.

Neto, V., and L. Bainer. "Mother and Wife Locked Up: A Day with the Family." Social Action Research Center, Calif.

New York Coalition for Juvenile Justice and Youth Services. "A Review of the Status of Post Foster Care Youth." The Runaway and Homeless Youth Advocacy Project, June 1982.

New York State Department of Corrections, "Westfield State Farm: Its History, Purpose, Make-up and Program."

New York State Division of Criminal Justice Services. "Female Offenders in New York State," Nov. 1982.

"On Prisons and Parenting: Preserving the Tie That Binds." *Yale Law Journal,* vol. 87, 1978.

Packard, Vance. *Our Endangered Children Growing Up in a Changing World*. Boston: Little, Brown, 1983.

Panichas, George. *The Courage of Judgment*. Knoxville: University of Tennessee Press, 1982.

Piaget, Jean. *The Moral Judgment of the Child*. New York: Free Press, 1965.

Postman, Neil. *The Disappearance of Childhood*. New York: Delacorte Press, 1982.

———. *Teaching as a Conserving Activity*. New York: Delacorte Press, 1979.

Potler, Cathy. "State of the Prisons. Conditions Inside the Walls." The Correctional Association of New York, March 1986.

Pray, Roger. "How Did Our Prisons Get That Way?" *American Heritage,* July/Aug. 1987.

Prescott, Peter S. *The Child Savers.* New York: Simon and Schuster, 1981.

Price, Barbara, and Natalie Sokoloff, eds. *The Criminal Justice System and Women: Women Offenders, Victims, Workers.* New York: Clark Boardman Co. Ltd., 1982.

"Prison Guards." *Penthouse,* April 1983.

Rafter, Nicole. *Partial Justice: Women in State Prisons 1800–1935.* Hanover, N.H.: New England University Press, 1985.

———, and Elena Natalizia. *The Criminal Justice System and Women.*

Rainwater, L. and Yancy. "The Moynihan Report and the Politics of Controversy." Cambridge, Mass.: MIT Press, 1967.

Rocawich, Linda. "Lock 'Em Up: America's All-Purpose Cure for Crime." *The Progressive,* Aug. 1987.

Rosenberg, Terry J. "Poverty in New York City: 1980–1985." Community Service Society of New York.

Rutter, Michael. *Maternal Deprivation Reassessed.* New York: Penguin Books, 1981.

Samenow, Stanton. *Inside the Criminal Mind.* New York: Times Books, 1984.

Sametz, Lynn. "Children of Incarcerated Mothers." *Social Work Journal,* July 1980.

Schecter, David. "Infant Development in Life Cycle and Its Common Vicissitudes."

"Sex Discrimination in Criminal Justice and Correctional Institutions." Public Meeting, State House Annex, Trenton, N.J., Dec. 1985.

Sherry, Peter. "The Charmed Life of Head Start." *The Public Interest,* Fall 1983.

Sizer, T. *Horace's Compromise.* Boston: Houghton Mifflin, 1984.

Spaulding, Edith, M.D. *An Experimental Study of Psychopathic Delinquent Women.* Rand McNally & Co., 1923. (Published for the Bureau of Social Hygiene.)

Spitz, René. *The First Year of Life.* New York: International University Press, 1965.

————. "Hospitalism: An Inquiry into the Genesis of Psychiatric Conditions in Early Childhood." In *Psychoanalysts Study Children.* New York: International University Press, 1945.

Stanton, Ann M. *When Mothers Go to Jail.* Lexington, Mass.: Lexington Books, 1980.

National Urban League. *The State of Black America 1986.*

————. *The State of Black America 1987.*

Steelman, Diane. "The Mentally Impaired in New York's Prisons." Correctional Association of New York, Jan. 1987.

————. "Toward a Crime Prevention Strategy." Correctional Association of New York, May 1985.

Stickney, Benjamin, and Virginia Plunkett. "Closing the Gap: A Historical Perspective on the Effectiveness of Compensatory Education." Bloomington, Ind.: Phi Delta Kappa, Inc., Dec. 1983.

"Study Finds Ratio of Retarded Higher in Jails than Outside," *New York Times,* June 13, 1982.

United States Department of Commerce, Bureau of Census. "Fertility of American Women." In *Population Characteristics,* 1982.

United States Department of Justice. "Assessing the

Relationship of Adult Criminal Careers to Juvenile Careers." Washington, D.C., 1982.

———. National Institute of Corrections. "Adult Female Offenders' Institutional Programs." In *Criminal Justice Planning.* Columbia: University of South Carolina, Feb. 1984.

Weidensal, Jean. *The Mentality of Criminal Women.* Baltimore: Warwick and York, 1916.

———. *Psychopathic Delinquent Women.*

Wertham, Frederick. *The Show of Violence.* New York: Greenwood Press, 1948.

"Who's Watching Our Children? The Latchkey Child Phenomenon." Senate Office of Research, State of California, Nov. 1983.

Wilson, James Q. *Thinking About Crime.* New York: Vintage Books, 1977.

World Health Organization. *Deprivation of Maternal Care: A Reassessment of Its Effects.* Geneva, 1962.

Index

305

310

312

About the Author

Jean Harris was born in Cleveland Heights, Ohio. She was educated at the Laurel School in Cleveland and at Smith College. She married James Scholes Harris and has two children, David and Jimmy. She spent three decades as a teacher and administrator. She ultimately became the headmistress of the Madeira School in McLean, Virginia. In 1966 she met Dr. Herman Tarnower and had a fifteen-year relationship with him—a relationship that ended tragically—and despite her denials, Jean Harris was convicted of killing Dr. Tarnower. She is now serving at Bedford Hills Correctional Facility the fifteen-years-to-life sentence that was meted out to her. She teaches and devotes hundreds of hours to the children who visit at the Children's Center.

THE PEOPLE BEHIND THE HEADLINES
FROM ZEBRA BOOKS!

PAT NIXON: THE UNTOLD STORY   (2300, $4.50)
by Julie Nixon Eisenhower
The phenomenal *New York Times* bestseller about the very private woman who was thrust into the international limelight during the most turbulent era in modern American history. A fascinating and touching portrait of a very special First Lady.

STOCKMAN: THE MAN, THE MYTH,
THE FUTURE   (2005, $4.50)
by Owen Ullmann
Brilliant, outspoken, and ambitious, former Management and Budget Director David Stockman was the youngest man to sit at the Cabinet in more than 160 years, becoming the best known member of the Reagan Administration next to the President himself. Here is the first complete, full-scale, no-holds-barred story of Ronald Reagan's most colorful and controversial advisor.

IACOCCA   (3018, $4.50)
by David Abodaher
He took a dying Chrysler Corporation and turned it around through sheer will power and determination, becoming a modern-day folk hero in the process. The remarkable and inspiring true story of a legend in his own time: Lee Iacocca.

STRANGER IN TWO WORLDS   (2112, $4.50)
by Jean Harris
For the first time, the woman convicted in the shooting death of Scarsdale Diet doctor Herman Tarnower tells her own story. Here is the powerful and compelling *New York Times* bestseller that tells the whole truth about the tragic love affair and its shocking aftermath.

Available wherever paperbacks are sold, or order direct from the Publisher. Send cover price plus 50¢ per copy for mailing and handling to Zebra Books, Dept. 2986, 475 Park Avenue South, New York, N.Y. 10016. Residents of New York, New Jersey and Pennsylvania must include sales tax. DO NOT SEND CASH.